THE MACMILLAN SHAKESPEARE
ADVISORY EDITOR: PHILIP BROCKBANK
Professor of English and Director of the
Shakespeare Institute, University of Birmingham
GENERAL EDITOR: PETER HOLLINDALE
Senior Lecturer in English and Education,
University of York

A MIDSUMMER NIGHT'S DREAM

THE MACMILLAN SHAKESPEARE

A MIDSUMMER NIGHT'S DREAM

Edited by

Norman Sanders

Professor of English, University of Tennessee

M

Macmillan Education

First published 1971
Reprinted 1976, 1977, 1978, 1979, 1982, 1984

Published by
MACMILLAN EDUCATION LTD
Houndmills Basingstoke Hampshire RG21 2XS
and London
Companies and representatives throughout the world

ISBN 0 333 02672 1

Printed in Hong Kong

CONTENTS

INTRODUCTION

I: *THE DATE OF A MIDSUMMER NIGHT'S DREAM*

As is the case with most Elizabethan plays, it is impossible to say with any degree of accuracy when *A Midsummer Night's Dream* was written; the only firm limit for its composition being set by a contemporary writer, Francis Meres, who in his book *Palladis Tamia: Wits Treasury*, lists it among those plays of Shakespeare which had been written before 1598. However, there are a number of details which appear to point to a date of writing sometime in the period late-1594 to 1595. Two passages in the play may be allusions to real events of the time. Titania's long speech at II. 1. 81–117 describing the unseasonable weather resulting from her quarrel with Oberon would fit the unusually bad three summers of 1594–6, especially perhaps the excessively cold and rainy one of 1594, which occasioned a good deal of contemporary comment. However, it should be noted that the passage does have an important dramatic function and is understandable by audiences who have no knowledge of the details of the English weather during the last ten years of Elizabeth's reign. The obvious comedy generated by the mechanicals' apprehension at introducing a lion into Theseus's Great Chamber in the course of their play has also been seen as a jocular allusion to a similar feat which led to the substitution of a blackamoor for a lion to draw a chariot during the festivities held at the Scottish Court on 30 August 1594 in honour of the baptism of Prince Henry, the heir of James VI. But again the episode needs no reference outside the play to raise its laughter.

Far less specific, though more convincing to those who know Shakespeare's works well, is the evidence of date provided by the style of the play. In it there has been detected, for the first time in Shakespeare's career in any sustained way, an employment of the poet's native lyric gifts for dramatic ends. The delight in the formal set speech, complex word-play, and descriptive passages, which characterise Shakespeare's early plays, are still present; but in *A Midsummer Night's Dream* they are under firm control with each change of metre and every variation of style, whether it be the dignified blank verse of Theseus, the artificial couplets of the lovers, the down-to-earth prose of the mechanicals, or the dancing rhythms of the fairies, necessary to produce some desired dramatic effect. These qualities, as well as similar themes, ideas, and preoccupations link the play to *Romeo and Juliet* and *Richard II*, the probable dates of which were 1594–6.

Closely related to discussions of the date of composition of the play is the speculation about the circumstances of its first performance; for some features of the play have suggested that it may have been written for a special occasion. To begin with, the title is very specific both for the time and its associations : Midsummer Night, 23 June, celebrated during the reign of Elizabeth as the Feast of Saint John the Baptist. It was a special season when mortals were thought to be the victims of both their own self-induced fancies and the tricks of mischievous fairies; it was also a time of revelling and of the practising by the young people of those ritual games aimed at determining one's partner in courtship and marriage. *A Midsummer Night's Dream*, it has been argued, would have been ideal for at least initial performance at some festive occasion which took place on this day already associated by long tradition with misrule and fun.

In following up the implications of this theory, some writers have stressed the strong emphasis on marriage: the keen anticipation of Theseus for his wedding with which the play opens; the mechanicals' playlet intended to be performed in its honour; the marital difficulties of the lovers, the triple ceremony celebrated in the last act, and the fairies' ritual to end the play and bring a supernatural blessing on the newly-weds and any future offspring they may have. And they have gone on to suggest that the play was written for a private performance in honour of some nobleman's marriage.

However, there is no strong external evidence to support such a theory, so that we must suppose that Shakespeare intended the play to be 'sundry times publicly acted by the Right Honourable the Lord Chamberlain his servants' (that is, by Shakespeare's own theatre company) as we are told by the title page of the first printed edition of the work.

II: THE SOURCES OF A MIDSUMMER NIGHT'S DREAM

It was Shakespeare's normal practice when composing a play to follow quite faithfully some printed version of the story or historical events he wished to dramatise. Sometimes his source was a novel (like Robert Green's *Pandosto* for *The Winter's Tale*), or an earlier play (such as the two-part *Troublesome Reign of King John* for his *King John*), or a chronicle history of England like that by Raphael Holinshed for his English history plays, or a vast historical biography like Plutarch's *Lives of the Noble Grecians and Romans* (which provided him with the materials for his Roman plays). But for *A Midsummer Night's Dream* there is no known source which would have furnished Shakespeare with his plot. The materials he used appear to have come from scattered recollections of his general reading together with his knowledge of English folk-lore and his observations of life.

He might well have read about Theseus and Hippolyta in the opening pages of Thomas North's translation of Plutarch's *Lives* and in Geoffry Chaucer's *The Knight's Tale* which begins with Theseus's victorious return from the wars with Hippolyta, and also deals with the rivalry

3

of two young men for the affections of the same girl. The
old romance of *Huon of Bordeaux* may have provided the
name and some details for the figure and rôle of Oberon;
even as Ovid's *Metamorphoses* seems to have been the
origin for the name of Titania, where it is used to describe goddesses descended from the Titans. The idea of
the magic potion and Bottom's transformation into an
ass have a number of literary parallels: some of them to
be found in works like Apuleius's *The Golden Ass* and
Reginald Scott's *The Discovery of Witchcraft* (1584),
which Shakespeare is known to have read.

The Pyramus and Thisbe story was a popular one
during the sixteenth century, being treated in at least
eleven different versions which were available to Shakespeare and which he may well have read while preparing
his own comic treatment of it. However, the idea for
producing humour by contrasting the tragic story with a
lumbering old-fashioned verse style may well have occur-
red to him while reading the version found in Arthur
Golding's translation of Ovid's *Metamorphoses*, which
was published in 1576, and which often sounds like a
product of Quince's own hand; for example,

Now as a t' oneside Pyramus, and Thisbe on the tother
Stood often drawing one of them the pleasant breath
                                        from other,
'O, thou envious wall,' they said, 'why let'st thou lovers
                                        thus?
What matters were it if that thou permitted both of us
In arms each other to embrace? Or if thou think that
                                        this
Were overmuch, yet mightest thou at least make room
                                        to kiss.'

Even after all possible literary sources for the play
have been traced, it is clear that those elements which
give it its special appeal were derived from unwritten
sources. The vivid, concrete details of the fairy world

obviously owe a great deal to the body of superstition, supernatural lore, and folk tales of the Warwickshire countryside into which the dramatist was born; even as Bottom and his crew of mechanicals strike us as having unaccountably strayed into the classical Athens of Theseus and his Amazonian queen from a recognisable sixteenth-century London.

III: *CRITICISM OF A MIDSUMMER NIGHT'S DREAM*

A Midsummer Night's Dream has never provoked the often violently opposed interpretations which characterise the criticism of most of Shakespeare's major plays. Most scholars are in agreement about such matters as the skilful organisation of the material, the different 'worlds' of the play, the kind of characterisation, the functional variety of the verse, and so on; the differences between their views rest in what they take to be Shakespeare's philosophical preoccupations. In view of this, an attempt has been made in the following paragraphs to discuss, first those aspects of the play on which there is general agreement, and then consider the principal critical opinions of the play's 'meaning'.

The Young Lovers Shakespeare's subjects are obviously love, courtship, marriage, and play-acting; and by extension the wider, more abstract implications of these topics: emotion, reason, judgement, imagination, illusion, reality, fancy. His poetic terminology for the treatment of love is derived from the idea expressed in the line 'Whoever loved and loved not at first *sight*?' For it is *sight* that is connected verbally with love in the play. Cupid's power is almost invariably projected in visual terms, because, as Theseus points out in the final scene, the capacity which the lover shares with the poet and the madman is a self-deluding imagination, which in his case takes the form of being able to 'see Helen's beauty in a brow of Egypt'. This note is struck much earlier, however, in the opening scene when Hermia wishes that her father looked but with her eyes, and Helena ruefully complains how

> Things base and vile, holding no quantity,
> Love can transpose to form and dignity. (ll. 232–3)

And from this point onwards the powers of seeing and loving are repeatedly interwoven, so that Demetrius is seen to err in 'doting on Hermia's eyes', Lysander is led to Helena's eyes when he is bewitched, and one of the girls envying the attractions of the other can say 'My eye should catch your eye. O, teach me how you look.' In view of this poetic fusion of ideas, it is easy to see that Oberon's magic juice, which causes love when it is 'on sleeping eyelids laid', and its antidote, derived from Diana's pansy, are something more than brilliant comic devices. They also make physical the ideas and attitudes found in the poetry, and permit a concrete working-out of the implications of the lovers' emotional convictions.

With his young lovers Shakespeare is obviously more interested in showing various attitudes to love than in arousing our interest in the individuals holding them. And because it is the situation that is important and not the people concerned in it, then 'character' in the sense it is applied to later comic creations like Portia (in *The Merchant of Venice*) or Beatrice (in *Much Ado About Nothing*) or Viola (in *Twelfth Night*) has little relevance in any discussion of these young Athenians. Certainly, Shakespeare makes some obvious distinctions between them. Helena is the taller of the two girls and she is blonde and fair-skinned in contrast to the smaller and darker Hermia. In their reactions too there is some contrast: Helena is the more conventionally feminine in her cowardice and lack of physical aggression, whereas Hermia can be stimulated by desperation to a fine display of shrewishness. Similarly Lysander is clearly the more idealistic and romantically impetuous of the two young men. But even in the theatre, where because of the differences between the actors, the personal distinctions are more obvious than on the printed page, there is no stress laid on them; and the emotional impact of the scenes in which the lovers appear is about the same as that produced by a dance of puppets. In fact, Puck's mistaking Lysander for Demetrius because of 'the Athenian garments he has on' is as fair a comment as one could wish for on the depth of their individual 'characters'.

Shakespeare's chief means of ensuring that the audience keeps its emotional distance from the predicament of the lovers and of preventing any speculation about them as real people is the style in which he makes them speak. It is stilted, artificial, verbally ingenious, full of false dignity, and elaborately inappropriate to the very ordinary emotions they are experiencing. For example, when Hermia is fearful and indignant at Lysander's desertion of her in the dark wood, she leisurely embroiders an idea in this way:

> The sun was not so true unto the day
> As he to me. Would he have stol'n away
> From sleeping Hermia? I'll believe as soon
> This whole earth may be bored, and that the
>   moon
> May through the centre creep, and so displease
> Her brother's noontide with th' Antipodes.
> (III. 2. 50–55)

And both Lysander's behaviour under the influence of the love potion and Helena's response to it are similarly artificial:

HELENA But who is here? – Lysander on the ground?
        Dead – or asleep? I see no blood, no wound.
        Lysander, if you live, good sir, awake!

LYSANDER [*Awaking*] And run through fire I will for thy
  sweet sake.
  Transparent Helena, Nature shows art,
  That through thy bosom makes me see thy heart.
  Where is Demetrius? O, how fit a word
  Is that vile name to perish on my sword!
HELENA Do not say so, Lysander, say not so.
  What though he love your Hermia? Lord! What
  though?
  Yet Hermia still loves you. Then be content.
LYSANDER Content with Hermia? No, I do repent
  The tedious minutes I with her have spent.
  Not Hermia but Helena I love;
  Who will not change a raven for a dove? (II. 2.
  109–120)

Such verse is charming, empty of any real emotional
conviction and perfectly suited to this group of young
people which provokes Puck's reaction:

  Shall we their fond pageant see?
  Lord, what fools these mortals be!
     (III. 2. 114–15)

The setting of the middle scenes also makes the lovers'
comic misunderstandings acceptable to the audience.
The night, the wood, and moonlight are appropriate as
natural surroundings for the lovers' imaginative states.
This is a time and place in the kind of light where 'easily
is a bush supposed a bear', and where the rapid changes
of emotion in the young people can appear as recollections of a dream; as Demetrius puts it:

  But, my good lord – I wot not by what power,
  But by some power it is – my love to Hermia,
  Melted as the snow, seems to me now
  As the remembrance of an idle gaud
  Which in my childhood I did dote upon
      (IV. 1. 162–6)

The environment of the wood at night, together with the intervention of Puck and Oberon has enabled Shakespeare to show us all the possible combinations in the pairing and opposing of the lovers until he can settle on the final stable arrangement in which all tastes are accounted for:

> That every man should take his own,
> In your waking shall be shown.
> Jack shall have Jill,
> Naught shall go ill,
> The man shall have his mare again, and all shall be well.
> (III. 2. 469–73)

This simple rural proverb defines the socially accepted and necessary grouping emerging from the adolescent process of love which we have witnessed.

It would be wrong to imply that Shakespeare intends the four lovers to be totally laughable and unserious. For romantic love is based upon the unique value of each human being, which in turn means that we must take seriously the element of choice in the selection of marriage partners. And without arousing too great an interest in it, Shakespeare is careful to include this aspect of any love affair. It is obvious that at the opening of the play the situation in which Hermia finds herself is potentially a tragic one, and is similar to the one which the genuinely tragic Juliet (in *Romeo and Juliet*) finds herself. Lysander gives exquisite expression to the fragility of love in lines which could well describe Juliet's fate:

> Or, if there were a sympathy in choice,
> War, death, or sickness did lay siege to it,
> Making it momentary as a sound,
> Brief as the lightning in the collied night,
> That, in a spleen, unfolds both heaven and earth,
> And – ere a man hath power to say, 'Behold!' –
> The jaws of darkness do devour it up;
> So quick bright things come to confusion.(I. 1. 141–9)

The possibility of human unhappiness is suggested here and the utterance is memorably pathetic; but the statement is so generalised that the personal involvement which tragedy demands is avoided so far as Hermia is concerned.

Theseus and Hippolyta The comic confusions experienced by the lovers in the central scenes are not self-contained, for the structure of the play ensures that they are related on a number of levels with the other character groups: Theseus and Hippolyta, the mechanicals, and the fairies. In the opening scene the romantic difficulties of the young lovers are contrasted with the love of Theseus and his Queen. These two older people are also in love and are impatient for their marriage-day as their opening exchange indicates – an exchange which is built on allusions to the moon, dreams, night, and wedding:

THESEUS Now, fair Hippolyta, our nuptial hour
> Draws on apace. Four happy days brings in
> Another moon – but O, methinks how slow
> This old moon wanes! She lingers my desires,
> Like to a stepdame or a dowager
> Long withering out a young man's revenue.

HIPPOLYTA Four days will quickly steep themselves in night,
> Four nights will quickly dream away the time;
> And then the moon – like to a silver bow
> New-bent in heaven – shall behold the night
> Of our solemnities.   (I. 1. 1–11)

But although the terminology here is similar to that associated with the lovers, there are two additional elements present: those of maturity and reasonableness. Throughout the first scene Theseus represents the spirit of reason and the forces of necessity. It is he who answers Hermia that rather than her father look with her eyes, she should 'with his judgment look', and who also gives voice to the demands of social order and the law.

In the scenes in the wood where Theseus is not present we are reminded of his rational viewpoint by the lovers themselves, who point to the irrationality of their attitudes by their own words. Helena, even before she leaves the court for the wood, attempts to justify her betrayal of the trust placed in her by Hermia and Lysander in this way:

> Love looks not with the eyes, but with the mind,
> And therefore is winged Cupid painted blind.
> Nor hath Love's mind of any judgment taste;
> Wings and no eyes figure unheedy haste;
> And therefore is Love said to be a child
> Because in choice he is so oft beguiled.
>
> (I. 1. 234-9)

And later the concept of 'love's reason' is given even clearer demonstration in Lysander's words and actions after his transformation:

> The will of man is by his reason swayed,
> And reason says you are the worthier maid.
> Things growing are not ripe until their season;
> So I, being young, till now ripe not to reason.
> And touching now the point of human skill,
> Reason becomes the marshal to my will
> And leads me to your eyes, where I o'erlook
> Love's stories written in Love's richest book.
>
> (II. 2. 121-8)

The Mechanicals   Comment on the nature of love as it is exemplified in the young people is also provided as Shakespeare draws into the wood his third group of human characters: Bottom and his crew. We have been introduced to these hard-handed Athenian workmen in the second scene of the play. Their object is to present an interlude to celebrate the wedding of Theseus, and they are thus ironically the only examples we see of the 'pert and nimble spirit of mirth' which the Duke calls for in the opening scene. In becoming actors and dramatists these men are choosing to move into a world of shadows and illusion which can only exist by virtue of the imaginative powers of the audience and players alike. Yet imagination is the one quality in which they are all woefully deficient; and much of the humour of the scene of their introduction lies in their assuming as little imagination in their audience as they have themselves. Nevertheless, the wood which is poetically associated with love, imagination, illusion, and transformation is an appropriate place for the rehearsal of their playlet which is by definition an experiment in these things.

Although the mechanicals do not make physical contact with the lovers, until the final scene, their dramatic activities, Bottom's transformation, and his experience with Titania provide implicit comment on the situation of the lovers. To begin with, the subject of their play is parallel to the situation of Hermia and Lysander: the story of Pyramus and Thisbe, parted by parental interference, who agree to flee their homes and meet at night. In their case, however, the outcome of their plan is tragic mistaking and resultant death, because unlike the Athenian lovers, the Classical pair have no supernatural manager like Oberon to make sure that tragedy is avoided. But even though at the story level *Pyramus and Thisbe* is 'tragical', the mechanicals' dramatic treatment of it makes its effect, as their prologue indicates, one of 'tragical mirth'.

Sometimes the contrast between the workmen and the lovers is achieved by theatrical arrangement. For example, in Act I, scene I the lovers decide to flout authority and violate social order as it is represented by Theseus. As they leave the stage, the mechanicals enter, speaking the strong prose of real life in contrast to the artificial couplets of the lovers. As they proceed to discuss their playlet with unimaginative literal-mindedness, we realise that behind their staging difficulties there lies a deep respect for order and right behaviour – two things the lovers have just been planning to thwart. Similarly, the scene of their first rehearsal follows Lysander's desertion of Hermia, and her vow 'either death or you I'll find immediately' is the cue for the mechanicals to enter 'pat, pat' at a marvellous convenient place for their trial run of a play about love and death. As their rôles are laboured through, one notes too that although the verse of the playlet is inferior to that spoken by the lovers, the difference is one of degree rather than kind.

It is, of course, in the character of Bottom that the major comment is made. Like Lysander and Demetrius he is, in his rôle of Pyramus, a lover, and like them he is a victim of fairy enchantment. Lysander's confusion between love and reason (quoted on page 11) is echoed far more sensibly by the weaver when he is the object of Titania's affections:

> Methinks, mistress, you should have little reason for that. And yet, to say the truth, reason and love keep little company together nowadays – the more the pity that some honest neighbours will not make them friends. (III. 1. 142–6)

Although, in being made physically into an ass, he is the most appropriately transformed of the wood's victims, Bottom's behaviour throughout his adventure is characterised by this basic common sense. He knows instinctively that his trouble lies in the wood and wishes only for 'wit enough to get out'. However, if he must remain, the extent of his effort at adjusting himself to his new circumstances is to stay sublimely himself and totally consistent to the unfamiliar tastes the ass-head forces upon him. As the lover of the Fairy Queen, Bottom is also connected with the mortal and supernatural governors of the play. On the one hand, he is the successor of Theseus who was the recipient of Titania's love as she led him through the glimmering night from a series of tragic love affairs; and on the other, he is a kind of mock-Oberon as he rules the fairies, sending them on errands which are a grotesque version of those for which the Fairy King employs Puck.

The Fairies   It is a stroke of comic irony that it should be Bottom, the grossest thick-skin among the humans, who alone knowingly comes into contact with the fairy world, which contains the fourth of the character-groups which make up the play's structure. In fashioning this supernatural world, Shakespeare needed to create a kind of second court which in the wood would parallel that of Theseus at the beginning and end of the play.

The fairy world is complete in itself, beautiful, ultimately benevolent, but containing mystery and a touch of the exotic, and more than a hint of disorder and destructive power. The dramatist drew his materials from a mixture of traditions: rustic fertility spirits, pagan gods, local pixies, Ovid's metamorphoses, the courtly masque. He varies the stress placed on each of these materials at different points in the play and sustains the whole in the imagination of the audience largely by his poetic powers.

The fairy rulers appear to be thought of as full-grown figures with great powers over the natural and human worlds. By allusion they are related to the orient, to mediaeval romance in their talk of knights and trains and pages, and with classical gods by their place in myths and their love affairs with mortals. Nowhere in the play are their capacities accurately defined, though these are clearly considerable. Titania can claim that summer attends upon her state, Oberon can order Puck to darken the night at will, and their quarrel can cause total seasonal havoc and thus serve as a large image of matrimonial and emotional discord. This is not, however, the only connection between the fairy rulers and the play's marriage theme; for one of the results of their quarrel is the bringing together of Titania and Bottom which has already been shown to be related to other parts of the play, and the reconciliation of Oberon and his Queen is followed by their joining together in the final scene to perform the masque of blessing the bride beds.

It is the attendants of Oberon and Titania in whom the uniqueness of Shakespeare's fairy world is located. The tininess of the creatures who can creep into acorn-cups, use grasshopper legs for tapers, and be deluged by the honey-bags of bees was derived by the dramatist from folk traditions; but it is his powerful evocation of such a world which started the literary and national tradition we have today. The achievement is the result of his skilful use of a large variety of poetic devices, only a few of which can be mentioned here. Most obviously, Shakespeare signals our entrance into the fairy world by the use of metrical variation. The trochaic tetrametre can be light and skipping in the mouth of the First Fairy:

> I do wander everywhere
> Swifter than the moon's sphere,
> And I serve the Fairy Queen,
> To dew her orbs upon the green. (II. 1. 6–9)

or mysteriously evocative of the night in Puck's song:

> Now the hungry lion roars,
>   And the wolf behowls the moon,
> Whilst the heavy ploughman snores,
>   All with weary task fordone. (V. 1. 363–6)

The couplet dialogue of the First Fairy and Puck in Act II scene 1 is quite different from that of the lovers; even as the slow-moving blank verse of Oberon and Titania has a music distinct from the poetry spoken by Theseus and Hippolyta. The detailed specificness of the fairy world comes in large part from the profusion of birds, insects, beasts, and flowers which pack the speeches; but also from the concrete depiction of the past events, visions, and landscapes with which they are associated. Each of the great 'set pieces' of description has the static, frozen quality of a finished pictorial masterpiece, whether it be Oberon's vision of Cupid (II. 1. 155–66) or Titania's description of her wait for the birth of her changeling boy (II. 1. 123–34), or Puck's account of his tricks among the villagers (II. 1. 47–57).

In the middle scenes of the play the vividness of the fairy world blends with the atmosphere of night, sleep, and wood to produce a complex stage image which has all the terrifying clarity of a nightmare of threat, discord, dissension, and destructive natural forces; but which possesses at the same time the blurred edges of a dream. This is the world where Puck and Oberon manipulate humans and supernatural creatures alike, and of which the atmosphere contrasts starkly with the clear lights of reason and day which characterise the Athens of Duke Theseus that anchors the play to reality at either end.

The Action and the Character Groups The two realms, Oberon's confusing wilderness and Theseus's orderly human society are the two poles on which the play's structure rests. As the action of the play unfolds, the groups of characters move between these two worlds, the general pattern being one which is common to many of Shakespeare's comedies: from a society orderly but filled with problems, through a natural wilderness, to emergence into the society of the first part newly harmonious and revitalised. Within this pattern there exists a series of different levels of awareness, intelligence, or consciousness. At the lowest level stands Bottom, supremely unaware of all that is happening, who with his unshakeable self-confidence leaves the wood unchanged

save by the recollection of his rare vision which will
do to provide Peter Quince with the material for a ballad.
Next above the mechanicals stand the lovers, also victims of fairy enchantment and of their own deluding
fancies rather than native stupidity. Above them is the
sphere of Theseus and Hippolyta, who experience neither
supernatural trickery nor self-deception, and so stand
outside the entanglements of the wood and the night to
pass judgement on the lovers' adventure. In fulfilling
this latter function a difference in the nature of their
awareness is reflected in their divergent attitudes.
Theseus dismisses the lovers' tale as an 'antique fable or
fairy toy', but his bride is struck by the curious consist-
ency of the four accounts:

> But all the story of the night told over,
> And all their minds transfigured so together,
> More witnesseth than fancy's images,
> And grows to something of great constancy;
> But howsoever, strange and admirable.
>
> (V. 1. 23–7)

Above the royal pair, by virtue of her powers, is Titania;
although she is below her lord and his servant by whom
she is tricked even as the lovers are. Finally, in all but
complete awareness, are Oberon and Puck; and beyond
them the audience who are alone in full possession of all
the knowledge in the play. But is this quite true? Or as
we watch the play within the play and perceive the confidence of the stage audience, are we reminded perhaps
that we too are an audience responding to a play behind
which stands the dramatist and his special powers of
poetic and theatrical enchantment of which we are the
willing victims?

The different levels of awareness within the play are
not as distinct or separate as the above tabulation suggests. Rather, as the four character groups are handled
we get a shifting interaction between them, each modify-

ing and qualifying the others. It is noticeable that Shakespeare formally introduces us to the four groups in the three opening scenes of the play so that the audience knows how the plot strands are to be divided.

Theseus and Hippolyta, with state and dignity, touch on their wedding, their love growing out of discord, and their intention to celebrate their nuptials with dramatic entertainment – in fact, broach the main matters of the whole play – in the opening scene. Egeus enters and shatters the mood with both his choppy, excited blank verse and his introduction of erotic disharmony, and thus effectively introduces the lovers' plot. The lovers themselves exchange their stilted couplets and make their plans which point ahead to the venue in the wood which is to occupy the middle scenes.

The second scene introduces the mechanicals and the topic and purpose of the playlet which drives them also to a future meeting in the forest. Thus all the human figures are presented and their destinations accounted for. But these two scenes look ahead not only to the centre of the play, but also to the final scene where all the characters will meet again, the celebration of the royal wedding being their ultimate point of contact. Then as we move to the wood in the second act, we find that the fairies' presence there is also accounted for by their attendance at Theseus's wedding.

From this point on the various strands of the plot are threaded, crossed, and juxtaposed. The Fairy King and Queen divide with the resulting natural disorder; the lovers' first act alignment is broken, they re-align and change again, shifting partners as though in some complicated dance routine; the mechanicals meet, are parted by Puck, and Bottom strides into his fairy dream. Finally Titania is undeluded and reconciled to her lord, the lovers sleep in their proper pairs, and Bottom is 'untranslated' and asleep beside them. As the dawn comes, the fairies vanish; the world of Theseus of the first scene invades the now daylit forest to dispel the confused dream with the horns of his huntsmen and with the sounds of his ideally matched pack of dogs, whose vocal harmony is the result of balancing basically disharmonious howls. As Theseus and Hippolyta depart, the lovers are left and attempt to define the curiously mixed sensations of reality and illusion which made up their forest dream:

DEMETRIUS   These things seem small and undistinguish-
      able,
      Like far-off mountains turned into clouds.
HERMIA   Methinks I see these things with parted eye,
      When everything seems double.
HELENA   So methinks;
      And I have found Demetrius, like a jewel,
      Mine own and not mine own.
DEMETRIUS   Are you sure
      That we are awake? It seems to me
      That yet we sleep, we dream. (IV. 1. 185–92)

In a no less masterly passage, Bottom attempts a comically dislocated prose definition of the same feeling of dream-cum nightmare, of beauty and horror, that his 'most rare vision' arouses in him.

In the final scene, marriage rites and theatrical events draw the various character groups together. But before this happens there is a moment of quiet deliberation as Theseus applies the cool eye of reason to 'what these lovers speak of'; and his conclusion is that it is 'more strange than true'. Hippolyta, however, is nearer to the truth, in the light of the audience's experience, when she describes the lovers' adventure as 'strange and admirable'. It is in her lines that the play comes closest to defining briefly the fact that the scenes in the wood have been for the young people both profoundly disturbing and imaginatively enriching.

As the tedious brief playlet of Pyramus and Thisbe

moves through its comic mistakings, mirroring the potential tragedy of the woodland scenes, the reaction of the stage audience to it is every bit as important as the behaviour of the wretched actors. Despite his casting of the poet as akin to the lover and the madman in his fanciful powers, Theseus proves to be an ideal playgoer; and he instructs his guests in their duties as spectators. Although the poor interlude is 'nothing, nothing in the world', he will hear it out because 'never anything can be amiss/When simpleness and duty tender it'. He knows too that the audience must exercise its imagination even as the actors theirs, and that

> If we imagine no worse of them than they of
> themselves, they may pass for excellent men.
>
> (V. I. 213–14)

As the simple-minded workmen grapple with their attempts to cope with the theatre world of shadows and illusions, we see on the stage an image of the theatrical experience of which we are a part; and we begin to realise what much of the play has been suggesting: the fragility of the dividing-line between the illusory and the real, the partial knowledge of the truth that any human being can hope to possess, the necessity for constant readjustment by all members of a society, the closeness of sleep and waking, the dangers of imaginative excess, the limitations of rational comprehension, the precariousness of human happiness, and the need for charity in all men.

As if to underline these distinctions and the delicate balance between them which Shakespeare has managed to achieve in his dream play, as the human characters leave the stage, it is the spirits of the night and the wood which have the last word. Theseus's world of order and reason is invaded by the beneficient fairies; and finally only Puck remains to dissolve for the dramatist the relationship between himself and his audience:

> If we shadows have offended,
> Think but this, and all is mended –
> That you have but slumbered here
> While these visions did appear.
> And this weak and idle theme,
> No more yielding but a dream,
> Gentles, do not reprehend.
> If you pardon, we will mend. (V. 1. 414–21)

Critical Views 'A delicate, tenuous piece of decoration.' This is how one writer has described *A Midsummer Night's Dream*, and his attitude might be taken as typical of most critics, who have been content to praise the play's delicacy, charm, and originality; but who appear to have been warned off subjecting it to anything like serious scrutiny by Bottom's flat statement that 'man is but an ass, if he go about to expound this dream'. However, in recent years some critics have had more confidence in the lasting quality of Shakespeare's art, and have realised that, as the play was a product of the same mind that conceived *King Lear*, *Hamlet*, and *Henry IV*, it is possible that this, along with the other mature comedies, may also possess a thematic seriousness of its own.

Most of the interpretations of the play's inner meaning are based on the conviction that it offers us a dramatic exploration of the nature of love and marriage; but there is a good deal of divergence of opinion as to the comic judgements implied. Some writers have seen the various character groups of the play interacting to produce a final affirmation of the value or 'truth' of human love, which, like the play itself, can only be perceived by the exercise of charity, generosity, and imagination. In this regard, much stress is laid upon the rich traditional folklore elements Shakespeare used and the fertility associations they have; so that the general movement of the action appears to be a natural one of blossoming, ripening, decaying, and renewing; or, in its human version, the emergence of maturity and marriage out of youthful fancy and infatuation, of the creative urge out of a disordered imaginative state.

Different aspects of romantic love have been detected in the play, and some critics have argued that Shakespeare favoured one at the expense of another. The lovers often emerge from such interpretations as the representatives of wildly fanciful and unreasonable affection which is a danger to proper social order; and the scenes devoted to them are often taken to be Shakespeare's satire of that kind of 'doting' that is divorced from reason, and must be purged through exposure to an unreal nightmare of chaos so that it may become reconciled to the demands of a rational society.

In most readings of the play as a moral treatise showing how irrational desire should be brought under the control of reason, Theseus and Hippolyta have come in for a good deal of praise. They appear in many accounts of the play as the touchstones of maturity, reality, and rational love and order, against which are set both the stupidities of the lovers and the pretensions of the mechanicals.

Rather more ambitious than such efforts to identify Shakespeare's ideas with one particular group of characters are those which try to fit all aspects of the play into a comprehensive scheme. A short summary of one such view will perhaps illustrate how this can be done. In the light of Renaissance ideas of what constitutes a proper marriage, all of the characters and their actions may be seen to have a larger symbolic meaning. The lovers at the outset lack reason in their behaviour and attitudes, and so wander appropriately in a wood of error; Theseus, as the personification of the higher power of love, has overcome Hippolyta, the unruly female passion, but fails in the application of charity in his treatment of Hermia and Lysander. In Oberon and

Titania we see worked on a supernatural plane what Theseus and Hippolyta represent on the human one: so that Oberon, by means of his magic, brings the irrational passions of Titania under his control in a right relationship after her episode with Bottom. Thus the ending of the play shows all the couples united, with Theseus teaching his wife and guests a lesson in imaginative charity in response to the playlet, and the fairy world, newly harmonious, blessing what is in fact a wedding of the rational and the animal parts of man.

While taking into account the topics of love and marriage, most critics have also given some importance to the theme of art – and more specifically of dramatic art. Because the play contains some discussion of the powers of the poet and his imagination and has also its own play within the play, it is often seen as a kind of comment on the theatrical experience itself. When looked at in this way, the widely different materials which make up the play and the great opposites it seems to suggest (like illusions and reality, sleeping and waking, reason and imagination) are seen to be transcended by Shakespeare's own art of dramatic composition.

Most criticism of the play contains useful ideas but none is completely convincing. This is because each critic, like each reader, brings to the play his own interests, values, and preoccupations. So that every reader must ultimately attempt his own interpretation – but he should do so with the reminder that as the miracle which is *A Midsummer Night's Dream* rests chiefly in the delicate balancing of all its parts, so too should any final interpretation of it.

IV: *A NOTE ON THE TEXT*

The first edition of *A Midsummer Night's Dream* was published by Thomas Fisher in 1600 and is usually known as the 'Fisher Quarto' or 'First Quarto'. This may have been set up from Shakespeare's own manuscript and is generally considered to be the authoritative text of the play. However, like most printed Elizabethan plays, it contains a number of errors, rather few stage directions, and some inconsistency in speech prefixes. Certain other irregularities in the text (such as mis-lineation of verse in the final scene and contradictions in details relating to the time scheme of the play) further suggest that Shakespeare may have revised the play at some time.

Some of the errors of the 1600 Quarto were corrected in a second quarto printed in 1619 but falsely dated 1600. This edition also introduced new errors and there were many changes in the spelling and punctuation.

A third edition of the play was included in the collected volume of Shakespeare's works known as the First Folio, which was prepared by two of Shakespeare's fellow actors and published in 1623. This text appears to have been printed from a copy of the Second Quarto of 1619 which had been altered in some respects by reference to a theatrical manuscript, Some of the readings in it correct errors found in the Quarto versions, and some are different but equally good versions of what the Quartos offer. It was this edition which first divided the play into acts.

The present text of the play is based on the First Quarto with the spelling and punctuation modernised. Where the Second Quarto obviously corrects the First, its readings have been adopted. Similarly, where the text of the First Folio makes better sense than the Quartos, its readings have been preferred. Errors common to all these early texts have been corrected after a study of the suggested emendations of eighteenth- and nineteenth-century editors.

The stage directions in the present text are expanded versions of those found in the early texts or original ones judged to be necessary to clarify the action for the modern reader.

A MIDSUMMER NIGHT'S DREAM

THE CHARACTERS

THESEUS, Duke of Athens
HIPPOLYTA, Queen of the Amazons, betrothed to
  Theseus
EGEUS, father of Hermia
HERMIA, daughter of Egeus, in love with Lysander
LYSANDER, in love with Hermia
DEMETRIUS, in love with Hermia
HELENA, in love with Demetrius
PHILOSTRATE, Master of the Revels to Theseus

PETER QUINCE, a Carpenter ('Prologue' in the interlude)
NICK BOTTOM, a Weaver ('Pyramus' in the interlude)
FRANCIS FLUTE, a Bellows-Mender ('Thisbe' in the inter-
  lude)
TOM SNOUT, a Tinker ('The Wall' in the interlude)
ROBIN STARVELING, a Tailor ('Moonshine' in the inter-
  lude)
SNUG, a Joiner ('The Lion' in the interlude)

OBERON, King of the Fairies
TITANIA, Queen of the Fairies
PUCK, or Robin Goodfellow
PEASE-BLOSSOM
COBWEB ⎫
MOTH ⎬ Fairies
MUSTARDSEED ⎭

Attendants on Theseus and Hippolyta
Other Fairies attending on Oberon and Titania

NOTES

Midsummer Night is the 23 June, and was associated by the Elizabethans with magic and certain folk customs (for which see Appendix pp. 176–9). It should be noticed, however, that Shakespeare is using associations and rituals in the play which were connected with May Day also. There is a similar blurring of time in the play. Theseus and Hippolyta at I. 1. 7–8 clearly expect to wait four days until their marriage ceremony, yet the action obviously takes place in three. This discrepancy is not noticed in the theatre, any more than the fact that the interlude of Pyramus and Thisbe takes much less time to perform than Theseus suggests at V. 1. 351–4, or that Puck 'puts a girdle round about the earth' in forty minutes, which is accounted for by his being off-stage for only seventy lines (see II. 1. 176–247).

ACT ONE, scene 1

The scene serves (1) to introduce the topics of love and marriage and establish the relationship of the two main human character groups to them; and (2) to set up the conditions for the rebellion of the young lovers and the reasons for their subsequent presence in the wood in II. 1 and 2. The exact location of this scene is not important; most probably the place is Theseus's palace. What is noteworthy is that the dream world of the wood and the night (II. 1 to IV. 1) is anchored here, as at the end of the play, by the daylit, rational world of Theseus's Athens.

4	lingers *postpones*
6	Long . . . revenue *Eating away a young man's income. The idea is of a son succeeding to his father's estate, but having to pay a regular income to his father's widow.*
7	steep themselves *be lost*
9–10	like . . . heaven *The reference is to the crescent shape of the new moon.*
13	pert *lively*
15	companion *fellow (used contemptuously)*
	pomp *ceremonious pageantry*

ACT ONE

Scene 1. *Enter* THESEUS, HIPPOLYTA, PHILOSTRATE, *and Attendants*

THESEUS Now, fair Hippolyta, our nuptial hour
　　　　Draws on apace. Four happy days bring in
　　　　Another moon – but O, methinks how slow
　　　　This old moon wanes! She lingers my desires,
　　　　Like to a stepdame or a dowager
　　　　Long withering out a young man's revenue.
HIPPOLYTA Four days will quickly steep themselves in
　　　　　night,
　　　　Four nights will quickly dream away the time;
　　　　And then the moon – like to a silver bow
　　　　New-bent in heaven – shall behold the night　　10
　　　　Of our solemnities.
THESEUS　　　　　Go, Philostrate,
　　　　Stir up the Athenian youth to merriments;
　　　　Awake the pert and nimble spirit of mirth;
　　　　Turn melancholy forth to funerals –
　　　　The pale companion is not for our pomp.
　　　　　　　　　　　　[*Exit* PHILOSTRATE
　　　　Hippolyta, I wooed thee with my sword
　　　　And won thy love doing thee injuries;
　　　　But I will wed thee in another key:
　　　　With pomp, with triumph, and with revelling.

Enter EGEUS *and his daughter* HERMIA, *and*
LYSANDER, *and* DEMETRIUS

EGEUS　　Happy be Theseus, our renownèd Duke.　　20
THESEUS Thanks, good Egeus. What's the news with
　　　　thee?
EGEUS　　Full of vexation come I, with complaint
　　　　Against my child, my daughter Hermia.
　　　　Stand forth, Demetrius. My noble lord,
　　　　This man hath my consent to marry her.

29

16–17   Hippolyta . . . injuries *One of Theseus's feats in Greek mythology was defeating the Amazons and capturing their queen, Hippolyta.*

18   in another key *in a different way. The image is musical and thus appropriate to a wedding.*

19   triumph *public festivity*

    Egeus *The name is pronounced with three syllables (Ee-gee-us).*

28   rhymes *love poems*

32   stol'n . . . fantasy *stealthily caused your image to be impressed on her imagination*

33   gauds *trinkets, toys*

    conceits *fanciful trifles*

34   Knacks *Knick-knacks, trifling gifts*

35   prevailment *persuasive power*

    unhardened *impressionable, not hardened by experience*

36   cunning *expert knowledge*

39   Be it so *If*

45   Immediately *Expressly*

46   Be advised *Consider*

51   leave the figure *allow your fair image to remain intact*

    disfigure *obliterate, destroy*

52   worthy *noble, honourable*

54   in this kind *in this regard*

    wanting *lacking*

    voice *consent*

30

Stand forth, Lysander. And, my gracious Duke,
This man hath bewitched the bosom of my
   child.
Thou, thou, Lysander, thou hast given her
   rhymes
And interchanged love-tokens with my child;
Thou hast by moonlight at her window sung,   30
With feigning voice, verses of feigning love,
And stol'n the impression of her fantasy
With bracelets of thy hair, rings, gauds,
   conceits,
Knacks, trifles, nosegays, sweetmeats –
   messengers
Of strong prevailment in unhardened youth.
With cunning hast thou filched my daughter's
   heart,
Turned her obedience, which is due to me,
To stubborn harshness. And, my gracious
   Duke,
Be it so she will not here before your Grace
Consent to marry with Demetrius,   40
I beg the ancient privilege of Athens:
As she is mine, I may dispose of her,
Which shall be either to this gentleman
Or to her death, according to our law
Immediately provided in that case.
THESEUS What say you, Hermia? Be advised, fair maid.
To you your father should be as a god;
One that composed your beauties – yea, and one
To whom you are but as a form in wax
By him imprinted, and within his power   50
To leave the figure or disfigure it.
Demetrius is a worthy gentleman.
HERMIA So is Lysander.
THESEUS   In himself he is;
But in this kind, wanting your father's voice,
The other must be held the worthier.

60   concern *be fitting to*

61   plead my thoughts *plead my case by giving expression to my own feelings and opinions*

63   may *can*

65   die the death *be legally executed*

68   Know of *Ascertain from*
         blood *passions*

70   livery *habit, dress*

71   aye *ever*
         mewed *incarcerated*

72   sister *a female member of a religious order*

73   moon *Diana, whose votaress Hermia would be, was the goddess of the moon and also the goddess of chastity.*

74   master their blood *control their passions*

75   pilgrimage *course of life*

76   earthlier happy *happier in an earthly way (as opposed to 'blessed')*
         rose distilled *Roses were used for the making of perfumes.*

80   patent *privilege*

81   his lordship *domination or control*

88   would *wishes*

89   protest *vow*

90   aye *ever*

HERMIA   I would my father looked but with my eyes.

THESEUS   Rather your eyes must with his judgment look

HERMIA   I do entreat your Grace to pardon me.
I know not by what power I am made bold,
Nor how it may concern my modesty   60
In such a presence here to plead my thoughts;
But I beseech your Grace that I may know
The worst that may befall me in this case
If I refuse to wed Demetrius.

THESEUS   Either to die the death, or to abjure
For ever the society of men.
Therefore, fair Hermia, question your desires,
Know of your youth, examine well your blood,
Whether, if you yield not to your father's
    choice
You can endure the livery of a nun,   70
For aye to be in shady cloister mewed,
To live a barren sister all your life,
Chanting faint hymns to the cold fruitless moon.
Thrice blessèd they that master so their blood
To undergo such maiden pilgrimage;
But earthlier happy is the rose distilled
Than that which, withering on the virgin thorn,
Grows, lives, and dies in single blessedness.

HERMIA   So will I grow, so live, so die, my lord,
Ere I will yield my virgin patent up   80
Unto his lordship whose unwishèd yoke
My soul consents not to give sovereignty.

THESEUS   Take time to pause; and by the next new
    moon –
The sealing day betwixt my love and me
For everlasting bond of fellowship –
Upon that day either prepare to die
For disobedience to your father's will,
Or else to wed Demetrius, as he would,
Or on Diana's altar to protest
For aye austerity and single life.   90

92   crazèd title *flawed claim*

98   estate *convey, settle on (as a property in law)*

99–110 I am ... man *It is possible that this speech is made in an aside to Theseus.*

99   well derived *nobly descended, well born*

100   possessed *furnished with rich possessions*

101   My fortunes ... ranked *My position and prosperity are of equally high standing*

102   with vantage *more so, better*

104   of *by*

105   prosecute *persevere or persist in*

106   avouch to his head *prove it to his face*

110   spotted *stained, marked (by his inconstancy)*

113   self-affairs *my own personal business*

114   my mind did lose it *it slipped my memory*

117   For *As for*
     arm *prepare*

118   fancies *thoughts of love*

120   extenuate *mitigate, soften*

122   What cheer *How is it with you*

123   go along *come with me*

124   business *This word is pronounced with three syllables.*

DEMETRIUS Relent, sweet Hermia; and, Lysander,
       yield
      Thy crazèd title to my certain right.

LYSANDER You have her father's love, Demetrius –
      Let me have Hermia's. Do you marry him.

EGEUS   Scornful Lysander! True, he hath my love,
      And what is mine my love shall render him;
      And she is mine, and all my right of her
      I do estate unto Demetrius.

LYSANDER I am, my lord, as well derived as he,
      As well possessed. My love is more than his; 100
      My fortunes every way as fairly ranked –
      If not with vantage – as Demetrius'.
      And – which is more than all these boasts can
        be –
      I am beloved of beauteous Hermia.
      Why should not I then prosecute my right?
      Demetrius – I'll avouch it to his head –
      Made love to Nedar's daughter, Helena,
      And won her soul; and she, sweet lady, dotes,
      Devoutly dotes, dotes in idolatry,
      Upon this spotted and inconstant man.   110

THESEUS I must confess that I have heard so much,
      And with Demetrius thought to have spoke
       thereof;
      But, being over-full of self-affairs,
      My mind did lose it. But, Demetrius, come;
      And come, Egeus; you shall go with me.
      I have some private schooling for you both.
      For you, fair Hermia, look you arm yourself
      To fit your fancies to your father's will;
      Or else the law of Athens yields you up –
      Which by no means we may extenuate –   120
      To death or to a vow of single life.
      Come, my Hippolyta. What cheer, my love?
      Demetrius and Egeus, go along;
      I must employ you in some business

125 Against *In preparation for*

126 nearly that concerns *which closely concerns*

129 How chance *How does it happen*

130 Belike *Probably*

131 Beteem *Allow, afford*
tempest of my eyes *storm of tears*

135 different in blood *upset by a difference in rank*

136 cross *perverse chance*

137 misgraffed *ill-matched*

138 spite *plague*

141–49 Or, if there ... confusion *This comparison seems to have been in Shakespeare's mind at this time, for it appears in a similar form in* Romeo and Juliet, *II. 2. 118–20. Line 149 could well be a description of the 'star-crossed' lovers of Verona.*

139 stood upon *was subject to*

143 momentany *momentary, transitory*

145 collied *dark, blackened*

146 spleen *sudden impulse due to passion*
unfolds *displays*

149 quick *vital (or perhaps 'quickly')*
confusion *destruction*

150 ever crossed *always thwarted*

151 edict *The accent is on the second syllable.*

152 teach ... patience *learn to accept our difficult lot with patience*

153 cross *difficulty*

155 fancy's *love's*

156 good persuasion *sound doctrine*

36

Against our nuptial, and confer with you
Of something nearly that concerns yourselves.

EGEUS With duty and desire we follow you.

[*Exeunt all but* LYSANDER *and* HERMIA

LYSANDER How now, my love? Why is your cheek so pale?
How chance the roses there do fade so fast?

HERMIA Belike for want of rain, which I could well   130
Beteem them from the tempest of my eyes.

LYSANDER Ay me! For aught that I could ever read,
Could ever hear by tale or history,
The course of true love never did run smooth;
But either it was different in blood –

HERMIA   O cross! Too high to be enthralled to low.

LYSANDER   Or else misgraffèd in respect of years –

HERMIA   O spite! Too old to be engaged to young.

LYSANDER   Or else it stood upon the choice of friends –

HERMIA   O hell! To choose love by another's eyes.   140

LYSANDER   Or, if there were a sympathy in choice,
War, death, or sickness did lay siege to it,
Making it momentany as a sound,
Swift as a shadow, short as any dream,
Brief as the lightning in the collied night,
That, in a spleen, unfolds both heaven and earth,
And – ere a man hath power to say, 'Behold!' –
The jaws of darkness do devour it up;
So quick bright things come to confusion.

HERMIA If then true lovers have been ever crossed,   150
It stands as an edict in destiny.
Then let us teach our trial patience,
Because it is a customary cross,
As due to love as thoughts, and dreams, and sighs,
Wishes, and tears – poor Fancy's followers.

LYSANDER A good persuasion. Therefore hear me, Hermia:

158   revenue *The accent is on the second syllable.*

159   remote *distant*

160   respects me *regards me*

165   without *outside*

167   To do . . . May *The celebration of the first day of May was a common practice in Elizabethan England, and the festivity was usually held in fields or woods. See the Appendix.*

168   stay *wait*

170   By his . . . head *Cupid was pictured as carrying in his quiver both a golden arrow with a sharp point which caused love and a blunt leaden one which repelled love. The source of the legend best known to the Elizabethans was Ovid's* Metamorphoses *which Shakespeare is known to have read.*

171   simplicity *innocence*

        Venus' doves *Compare* Venus and Adonis (*1593*): 'her silver doves, by whose swift aid/Their mistress, mounted, through the empty skies/In her light chariot quickly is conveyed.'

173–4   And by that fire . . . seen *The reference is to Virgil's* Aeneid *in which Dido, Queen of Carthage, burns herself to death when her lover, the Trojan Aeneas, deserts her in order to found Rome.*

180   God speed *May God prosper you*

182   fair *beauty. It is clear from III. 2. 259 and 292 that Hermia is dark haired and skinned and is short in height, and, from III. 2. 188 and 294–6 that Helena is fair and tall. There is some evidence from Shakespeare's plays that his acting company, the Lord Chamberlain's Men, had two boys so distinguished at this time.*

183   lodestars *pole stars (which guide travellers)*

        air *music*

184   tuneable *tuneful, melodious*

186   favour *features, good looks*

I have a widow aunt, a dowager
Of great revenue; and she hath no child.
From Athens is her house remote seven leagues;
And she respects me as her only son.   160
There, gentle Hermia, may I marry thee;
And to that place the sharp Athenian law
Cannot pursue us. If thou lov'st me then,
Steal forth thy father's house to-morrow night;
And in the wood, a league without the town –
Where I did meet thee once with Helena,
To do observance to a morn of May –
There will I stay for thee.

HERMIA   My good Lysander,
I swear to thee by Cupid's strongest bow,
By his best arrow with the golden head,   170
By the simplicity of Venus' doves,
By that which knitteth souls and prospers loves,
And by that fire which burned the Carthage
    queen
When the false Trojan under sail was seen,
By all the vows that ever men have broke –
In number more than ever women spoke –
In that same place thou hast appointed me
To-morrow truly will I meet with thee.

LYSANDER Keep promise, love. Look, here comes
    Helena.

Enter HELENA

HERMIA God speed, fair Helena! Whither away?   180
HELENA Call you me fair? That 'fair' again unsay.
Demetrius loves your fair. O happy fair!
Your eyes are lodestars, and your tongue's sweet
    air
More tuneable than lark to shepherd's ear,
When wheat is green, when hawthorn buds
    appear.
Sickness is catching. O, were favour so,

187   ere *before*

188–9   My ear . . . melody *My ear would learn the tone of your voice; my eye copy the way you look; my tongue should emulate the way you speak.*

190   bated *subtracted, excepted*

191   translated *transformed*

193   sway the motion *control the impulses*

201   Would *If only*

206   graces *precious qualities*
        love *lover*

207   That he . . . hell *Athens is now a place of torment to me since it is where I cannot marry Lysander.*

209   Phoebe *Diana, the goddess of the moon and of chastity*

210   glass *mirror*

211   pearl *pearls*

212   still *ever, always*

213   Athens' *It is possible that this is a noun being used as an adjective; compare line 173 'Carthage queen'.*
        devised *planned*

214–16   And in . . . sweet *The idealised picture of girlish friendship is later elaborated in III. 2. 198–219, and provides an ironic backcloth to their quarrel which breaks out when they feel that their love affairs are affected by it.*

215   faint *pale in colour (?), delicate of odour (?)*
        wont *accustomed*

216   counsel *secret thoughts*

Yours would I catch, fair Hermia, ere I go.
My ear should catch your voice, my eye your
    eye,
My tongue should catch your tongue's sweet
    melody.
Were the world mine, Demetrius being bated, 190
The rest I'd give to be to you translated.
O, teach me how you look, and with what art
You sway the motion of Demetrius' heart.

HERMIA I frown upon him, yet he loves me still.

HELENA O that your frowns would teach my smiles
    such skill!

HERMIA I give him curses, yet he gives me love.

HELENA O that my prayers could such affection move!

HERMIA The more I hate, the more he follows me.

HELENA The more I love, the more he hateth me.

HERMIA His folly, Helena, is no fault of mine.   200

HELENA None but your beauty. Would that fault were
    mine!

HERMIA Take comfort. He no more shall see my face;
Lysander and myself will fly this place.
Before the time I did Lysander see,
Seemed Athens as a paradise to me.
O, then, what graces in my love do dwell,
That he hath turned a heaven unto a hell!

LYSANDER Helen, to you our minds we will unfold.
To-morrow night, when Phoebe doth behold
Her silver visage in the watery glass,   210
Decking with liquid pearl the bladed grass –
A time that lovers' flights doth still conceal –
Through Athens' gates have we devised to
    steal.

HERMIA And in the wood, where often you and I
Upon faint primrose beds were wont to lie,
Emptying our bosoms of their counsel sweet,
There my Lysander and myself shall meet,
And thence from Athens turn away our eyes

219   stranger companies *the companionship of strangers. All the early editions of the play have 'strange companions' at this point.*

222   Keep word *Hold to your promise*

223   lovers' food *i.e. the sight of each other*

226   other some *other people*

232–3   Things . . . dignity *It is just this effect that the love potion works in Titania in III. i and IV. 1.*

232   holding no quantity *having no proportion, shapeless*

233   transpose *transform*
         dignity *worth, value*

234   Love . . . mind *Love does not accept the evidence of the senses but is determined by figments of the imagination.*

236   of any judgment taste *any touch of reason. Compare Bottom's version of the same idea in III. 1. 143–4.*

237   wings and no eyes *The traditional conception of Cupid was a blind, winged boy or child.*
         figure *symbolise*

240   waggish *playful*

242   eyne *eyes*

248   intelligence *piece of information*

249   it is a dear expense *'to Demetrius it will cost a great deal even for him to thank me', but for Helena it is a 'trouble worth taking'. There is almost certainly also a pun intended on 'dear' meaning 'precious'.*

250   enrich my pain *reward myself richly for my pains*

To seek new friends and stranger companies.
Farewell, sweet playfellow. Pray thou for us; 220
And good luck grant thee thy Demetrius.
Keep word, Lysander. We must starve our
   sight
From lovers' food till morrow deep midnight.
LYSANDER I will, my Hermia.

                        [*Exit* HERMIA
               Helena, adieu!
   As you on him, Demetrius dote on you.

                                    [*Exit*
HELENA How happy some o'er other some can be!
   Through Athens I am thought as fair as she.
   But what of that? Demetrius thinks not so;
   He will not know what all but he do know.
   And as he errs, doting on Hermia's eyes, 230
   So I, admiring of his qualities.
   Things base and vile, holding no quantity,
   Love can transpose to form and dignity.
   Love looks not with the eyes, but with the mind,
   And therefore is winged Cupid painted blind.
   Nor hath Love's mind of any judgment taste;
   Wings and no eyes figure unheedy haste;
   And therefore is Love said to be a child
   Because in choice he is so oft beguiled.
   As waggish boys in game themselves forswear, 240
   So the boy Love is perjured everywhere;
   For ere Demetrius looked on Hermia's eyne
   He hailed down oaths that he was only mine,
   And when this hail some heat from Hermia felt,
   So he dissolved, and showers of oaths did melt.
   I will go tell him of fair Hermia's flight.
   Then to the wood will he to-morrow night
   Pursue her; and for this intelligence
   If I have thanks, it is a dear expense.
   But herein mean I to enrich my pain, 250
   To have his sight thither and back again.   [*Exit*

ACT ONE, scene 2

*This scene introduces the third of the human character
groups, establishes their connection with the marriage theme
through their intention to produce a play for Theseus's
wedding, and prepares for their presence in the wood in III.1.
There is no specific location for the scene: it is simply some-
where in Athens, perhaps Quince's house. As is common in
Shakespeare and other Elizabethan dramatists, the characters of lower social levels speak prose in general.*

All the tradesmen are appropriately named:

Snout	*for the spout of a kettle;*
Quince	*from 'quoins' or 'quines', wedge-shaped pieces of wood used in building;*
Snug	*for the tightness of joints necessary in wood-work;*
Bottom	*for the reel on which thread was wound during weaving;*
Flute	*for the sound made by bellows, or perhaps after fluted church organs which he would be called upon to repair;*
Starveling	*because tailors were proverbial for their thin-ness.*

2	You were best *It would be best for you to*
	generally *Bottom means 'severally', that is 'sepa-rately'. The line is Shakespeare's device for intro-ducing the characters to the audience.*
3	scrip *written list*
4	scroll *1 narrow paper wound round two rollers, apparently used for the players' parts in the theatres of the time*
5	interlude *a short play. This was the usual word used in England to describe a dramatic entertainment of any sort up to about 1570.*
9	treats on *deals with*
10	grow to a point *arrive gradually at a conclusion*
11	Marry *An exclamation, originally meaning 'By the Virgin Mary'.*
11–12	The Most . . . Thisbe *This title parodies those typical*

44

Scene 2. *Enter* QUINCE *the carpenter, and* SNUG *the joiner,
and* BOTTOM *the weaver, and* FLUTE *the bellows-mender,
and* SNOUT *the tinker, and* STARVELING *the tailor*

QUINCE   Is all our company here?

BOTTOM   You were best to call them generally, man by
man, according to the scrip.

QUINCE   Here is the scroll of every man's name which
is thought fit through all Athens to play in our interlude before the Duke and the Duchess on his
wedding day at night.

BOTTOM   First, good Peter Quince, say what the play
treats on; then read the names of the actors; and so
grow to a point.   10

QUINCE   Marry, our play is *The Most Lamentable
Comedy and Most Cruel Death of Pyramus and
Thisbe.*

BOTTOM   A very good piece of work, I assure you, and
a merry. Now, good Peter Quince, call forth your
actors by the scroll. Masters, spread yourselves.

QUINCE   Answer as I call you. Nick Bottom, the
weaver?

BOTTOM   Ready! Name what part I am for, and
proceed.   20

QUINCE   You, Nick Bottom, are set down for Pyramus.

BOTTOM   What is Pyramus? – a lover or a tyrant?

QUINCE   A lover that kills himself, most gallant, for
love.

BOTTOM   That will ask some tears in the true perform-
ing of it. If I do it, let the audience look to their eyes!
I will move storms; I will condole in some measure.
To the rest. – Yet my chief humour is for a tyrant. I
could play Ercles rarely, or a part to tear a cat in, to
make all split: 30

> 'The raging rocks
> And shivering shocks

of tragedies written during the 1560–70s; for example, Thomas Preston's Cambises is called 'a, lamentable tragedy mixed full of pleasant mirth' and Richard Edwards' named his play Damon and Pithias 'a tragical comedy' because it 'mixed mirth with care'.

12   Pyramus and Thisbe See Introduction, p. 4.

16   Masters, spread yourselves It is not certain what action is indicated here. In modern productions sometimes the actors are seated spread out on a bench, or sit down stretched out on the floor, or they are spread out in a line and step forward as their names are called.

26   let the . . . eyes the audience had best take care that they do not weep their eyes out

27   condole express grief, lament

28   To the rest Continue with the roll call

humour This could mean either 'whims' or 'natural inclination'.

tyrant This was a very popular rôle beginning with the character of Herod in the biblical Mystery plays of the fourteenth and fifteenth centuries. Other examples are King Cambises, Christopher Marlowe's Tamburlaine, and Shakespeare's own Richard III.

29   Ercles Hercules. Although there is no play in existence with a ranting part for this character there are references by contemporaries of Shakespeare to actors 'thundering the twelve labours of Hercules'.

a part . . . cat in A proverbial saying for an acting rôle that requires ranting and bombast.

30   to make all split to make the speech and actions boisterous like a sea wrecking a ship; or to reduce the audience to emotional wrecks (?)

31–8   The raging . . . Fates This is almost certainly Shakespeare parodying the style of what he knew as the old-fashioned plays of the 1570s. The lines are very similar to those found in two passages of John Studley's translation of Seneca's Hercules Oetaeus (1581).

35   Phibbus' car Bottom's mispronunciation of 'Phoebus' car', the chariot of the sun-god Phoebus Apollo.

40   vein manner, mode

41   condoling pathetic

45   wandering knight knight-errant; like the tyrant this was a popular dramatic rôle.

46

> Shall break the locks
>> Of prison gates,
> And Phibbus' car
> Shall shine from far,
> And make and mar
>> The foolish Fates.'

This was lofty! – Now name the rest of the players. – This is Ercles' vein, a tyrant's vein; a lover is more 40 condoling.

QUINCE Francis Flute, the bellows-mender?

FLUTE Here, Peter Quince.

QUINCE Flute, you must take Thisbe on you.

FLUTE What is Thisbe? – a wandering knight?

QUINCE It is the lady that Pyramus must love.

FLUTE Nay, faith, let not me play a woman – I have a beard coming.

QUINCE That's all one: you shall play it in a mask, 50 and you may speak as small as you will.

BOTTOM An I may hide my face, let me play Thisbe too. I'll speak in a monstrous little voice: 'Thisne, Thisne!' 'Ah, Pyramus, my lover dear! Thy Thisbe dear, and lady dear!'

QUINCE No, no; you must play Pyramus; and, Flute, you Thisbe.

BOTTOM Well, proceed.

QUINCE Robin Starveling, the tailor?

STARVELING Here, Peter Quince. 60

QUINCE Robin Starveling, you must play Thisbe's mother. Tom Snout, the tinker?

SNOUT Here, Peter Quince.

QUINCE You, Pyramus' father; myself, Thisbe's father; Snug, the joiner, you the lion's part; and I hope here is a play fitted.

SNUG Have you the lion's part written? Pray you, if it be, give it me; for I am slow of study.

48   let me . . . woman *In the Elizabethan theatres female parts were played by boys and young men.*

50   That's all one *That makes no difference*

       play . . . mask *This may be an indication that Thisbe's rôle is to be played in a woman's mask; or the reference may be to the face covering that many Elizabethan women wore as part of their everyday dress to protect their complexions against the sun.*

51   small *softly*

52   An *If*

53–4   Thisne, Thisne! *Bottom is here attempting to pronounce an affectionate diminutive of the name in order to lead into a display of his ability to produce the requisite 'little voice' in Thisbe's reply to her lover's call. Some critics have claimed that the word means 'in this manner'; however, the repetition casts doubt on this suggestion.*

61–4   Thisbe's mother . . . father *Neither of these characters are mentioned again and they do not appear in the rehearsal or the play when it is performed in V. 1. Some scholars have tried to find plausible reasons for their omission, but inconsistencies of detail such as this are common in all Shakespeare's plays.*

66   fitted *cast*

68   am slow of study *have difficulty in learning by heart*

69   extempore *with no advanced preparation*

73   that *so that*

81   aggravate *Bottom means 'moderate', i.e. reduce, lessen.*

82   roar you *This grammatical form was often used by the uneducated classes. The sense here is 'roar for you'.*

       sucking *young, unweaned*

83   an 'twere *as if it were*

84–8   for Pyramus . . . Pyramus *This is often played on the stage as gross flattery designed to molify Bottom sulking because he cannot play the lion's part.*

85   sweet-faced *This phrase may be suggested by Bottom's scowling; see note to ll. 84–8.*

       a proper man *as handsome a man*

92–5   I will . . . yellow *Bottom here displays his weaver's knowledge of dyeing.*

93   orange-tawny *dark yellow*

       purple-in-grain *dyed fast with a purple or red colour*

96   French-crown-colour *light yellow like the colour of the French gold coin, the* écu

QUINCE You may do it extempore; for it is nothing
but roaring.   70

BOTTOM Let me play the lion too. I will roar that I
will do any man's heart good to hear me. I will roar
that I will make the Duke say, 'Let him roar again,
let him roar again.'

QUINCE An you should do it too terribly you would
fright the Duchess and the ladies that they would
shriek; and that were enough to hang us all.

ALL   That would hang us, every mother's son.

BOTTOM I grant you, friends, if you should fright the
ladies out of their wits they would have no more   80
discretion but to hang us. But I will aggravate my
voice so that I will roar you as gently as any sucking
dove. I will roar you an 'twere any nightingale.

QUINCE You can play no part but Pyramus; for
Pyramus is a sweet-faced man; a proper man as one
shall see in a summer's day; a most lovely, gentle-
man-like man. Therefore you must needs play
Pyramus.

BOTTOM Well, I will undertake it. What beard were I
best to play it in?   90

QUINCE Why, what you will.

BOTTOM I will discharge it in either your straw-colour
beard, your orange-tawny beard, your purple-in-
grain beard, or your French-crown-colour beard,
your perfect yellow.

QUINCE Some of your French crowns have no hair at
all; and then you will play barefaced! But, masters,
here are your parts, and I am to entreat you, request
you, and desire you to con them by to-morrow night,
and meet me in the palace wood a mile without the   100
town, by moonlight. There will we rehearse; for if
we meet in the city we shall be dogged with company, and our devices known. In the meantime I will
draw a bill of properties such as our play wants. I
pray you, fail me not.

96–7   Some of . . . at all *The reference here is to baldness produced by venereal disease which was associated by the Elizabethans with France and Italy.*

96   crowns *heads*

97   barefaced *both 'without a beard' and 'in an embarrassed fashion'*

98   am to *must*

99   con *learn by heart, memorise*

100   without *outside*

103   devices *plans*

104   bill *list*
        properties *stage furnishings*

107   obscenely *As in l. 81, Bottom again uses the wrong word. What he intends is not certain and many scholars compare Costard's misuse of the same word to mean 'seemly' in* Love's Labour's Lost, *IV. 1. 136 'When it comes so smoothly off, so obscenely, as it were, so fit'. However, in view of the context, Bottom may intend the meaning 'so as not to be seen'.*

108   perfect *word-perfect in your parts*

110   hold or cut bow-strings *hold to your promise to be there or break your word and be disgraced (?). The expression is obviously connected with archery, but the exact meaning of the phrase is not known.*

BOTTOM We will meet, and there we may rehearse most obscenely and courageously. Take pains, be perfect. Adieu!

QUINCE At the Duke's oak we meet.

BOTTOM Enough; hold or cut bow-strings.   110

                           [*Exeunt*

ACT TWO, scene 1

The place of this scene is the wood mentioned by Lysander in I. 1. 165 and Quince in I. 2. 90. The time is the night of the day following that on which I. 1 and I. 2 take place. The scene introduces the Fairies, accounts for their presence in Athens, establishes the cause of discord between Oberon and Titania, and makes the first dramatic connection between the Fairies and the Lovers.

at one door . . . another *Stage directions in Elizabethan plays indicating entrance and exit frequently note how the two doors at the rear or back sides of the stage should be used.*

Puck *The word means 'imp, devil'. In the early editions of the play the character is often referred to in the stage directions and speech prefixes and dialogue as 'Robin Goodfellow'; for his characteristics, see Appendix, pp. 176–9. One of his stage appearances is described in an anonymous play* Grim the Collier of Croyden (*written about 1600*): 'Enter Robin Goodfellow, in a suit of leather close to his body; his face and hands coloured russet-colour, with a flail.'

2 ff.　　Over hill . . . *Shakespeare marks the first appearance of the fairy world in the play by a four-stress verse form different from the blank verse of the lovers and Theseus, and in marked contrast to the prose of the mechanicals who have just left the stage.*

3　　Thorough *Through. The old form of the word is retained here for the sake of the metre.*

4　　park *land fenced to contain game*
　　pale *enclosed land*

7　　moon's sphere *In Elizabethan astronomy the moon was fixed to a hollow crystalline sphere which was concentric with the earth and which revolved around the earth once per day.*

9　　her orbs *fairy rings; circles of darker or higher grass thought to be formed by fairy dancing.*

10　　pensioners *The allusion is to the fifty young male courtiers, 'the gentlemen-pensioners', dressed in splendid uniforms, who attended Queen Elizabeth as her personal body-guard.*

ACT TWO

Scene 1. *Enter a* FAIRY *at one door, and* PUCK (ROBIN GOODFELLOW) *at another*

PUCK How now, spirit; whither wander you?

FAIRY Over hill, over dale,
   Thorough bush, thorough brier,
  Over park, over pale,
   Thorough flood, thorough fire –
  I do wander everywhere
  Swifter than the moon's sphere,
  And I serve the Fairy Queen,
  To dew her orbs upon the green. ~~fairy lines~~
  The cowslips tall her pensioners be; 10
  In their gold coats spots you see –
  Those be rubies, fairy favours;
  In those freckles live their savours.
 I must go seek some dewdrops here,
 And hang a pearl in every cowslip's ear.
 Farewell, thou lob of spirits; I'll be gone.
 Our Queen and all her elves come here anon.

PUCK The King doth keep his revels here to-night.
 Take heed the Queen come not within his sight,
 For Oberon is passing fell and wrath 20
 Because that she as her attendant hath
 A lovely boy, stol'n from an Indian king.
 She never had so sweet a changeling,
 And jealous Oberon would have the child
 Knight of his train, to trace the forests wild;
 But she perforce witholds the lovèd boy,
 Crowns him with flowers and makes him all her
  joy.
 And now they never meet in grove or green,
 By fountain clear, or spangled starlight sheen,
 But they do square, that all their elves for fear 30
 Creep into acorn cups and hide them there.

12	favours *love tokens, jewels*
13	savours *perfumes*
15	hang ... ear *In Elizabethan England the practice of wearing a pearl drop in the lobe of the ear was both a male and female habit.*
16	lob *lubber, lout (in contrast with the tiny, aetherial fairies)*
17	anon *in a short time*
20	passing *surpassingly, exceedingly*
	fell *fierce, angry*
22	Indian *Oberon and Titania are also associated with India at ll. 69 and 124.*
23	changeling *The word is pronounced in three syllables. Usually it is applied to the child left in place of a baby kidnapped by fairies; but here it means the stolen child.*
24	jealous *envious*
25	trace *traverse, range through*
26	perforce *forcibly*
29	sheen *bright shining*
30	square *confront each other in a hostile manner*
	that *so that*
32	making *appearance*
	quite *completely*
33	shrewd *mischievous*
35–9	frights ... harm *These are all tricks traditionally associated with Robin Goodfellow.*
35	villagery *villages or villagers*
36	Skim milk *Puck does this in order to steal the cream.*
	quern *handmill for grinding corn. Puck sometimes hindered such operations.*
37	bootless *fruitlessly (because Puck prevents the milk from becoming butter)*
38	barm *head or froth on ale*
40	Hobgoblin *literally 'Robert or Robin the goblin'*
45	bean-fed *fed on horse-beans or field-beans*
	beguile *trick*
47	gossip *old woman, crony; originally the term was restricted to a sponsor in baptism or to a midwife.*
48	crab *crab-apple; often roasted and put in warm ale to form a drink called a 'posset'.*
50	dewlaps *slack skin beneath the chin of an old person*
51	aunt *old woman*
	saddest *most serious*

54

FAIRY Either I mistake your shape and making quite,
Or else you are that shrewd and knavish sprite
Called Robin Goodfellow. Are not you he
That frights the maidens of the villagery,
Skim milk, and sometimes labour in the quern,
And bootless make the breathless housewife
    churn,
And sometime make the drink to bear no barm,
Mislead night-wanderers, laughing at their
    harm?
Those that 'Hobgoblin' call you and 'Sweet
    Puck',   40
You do their work, and they shall have good
    luck.
Are not you he?

PUCK   Thou speakest aright:
I am that merry wanderer of the night.
I jest to Oberon, and make him smile
When I a fat and bean-fed horse beguile,
Neighing in likeness of a filly foal;
And sometimes lurk I in a gossip's bowl
In very likeness of a roasted crab;
And when she drinks, against her lips I bob,
And on her withered dewlap pour the ale.   50
The wisest aunt, telling the saddest tale,
Sometime for three-foot stool mistaketh me
Then slip I from her bum. Down topples she,
And 'Tailor!' cries, and falls into a cough;
And then the whole choir hold their hips and
    laugh,
And waxen in their mirth, and neeze, and
    swear
A merrier hour was never wasted there.
But room, Fairy! Here comes Oberon.

FAIRY And here my mistress. Would that he were
    gone!

54   And 'Tailor' cries *A common custom of unknown origin; possibly because the person who falls is like a tailor (sitting on the floor). There may also be a pun on 'tail' (on which one falls).*

55   choir *company; perhaps here with the idea of a 'chorus laughers' (?)*

56   waxen *increase (in loudness)*
           neeze *sneeze*

57   wasted *passed, spent*

58   room *make way*

59   Enter ... hers *See note to the scene's initial stage direction.*
           Titania *Shakespeare's pronunciation ·was probably 'Tight-aynia'.*

61   jealous *envious*
           Fairy *i.e. the Fairy who has been talking to Puck*

63   rash wanton *hasty and headstrong creature*

64   Then I ... lady *Titania implies that if what Oberon says is true then she should be the mistress of his affections which she proceeds to contradict in ll. 65–73.*

64–5   know When *know of times when*

66   Corin *Type-name for the love-sick shepherd in pastoral love poetry.*

67   pipes of corn *pipes made of wheat or oat stalks*
           versing *singing, composing love songs*

68   Phillida *Type-name for the beloved shepherdess in pastoral love poetry.*

69   steep *steep mountain (in the Himalayas ?). The earliest text of the play reads 'steppe'.*

70   bouncing *physically hearty*
           Amazon *i.e. Hippolyta*

71   buskined *wearing leather hunting boots or buskins. Hippolyta was a famed huntress as well as a warrior queen.*

75   Glance at *reflect upon*

77–80   Didst ... Antiopa? *Shakespeare apparently took these names from Thomas North's translation of Plutarch's Life of Theseus.*

78   Perigenia *Perigouna, daughter of Synnis, whom Theseus slew, was seduced by Theseus after her father's death and became the mother of Melanippus.*
           ravishèd *abducted*

79   Aegles *A nymph, the daughter of Panopeus, for whom Theseus forsook Ariadne and whom he later deserted.*

Enter OBERON, *the King of Fairies, at one door,
with his Train; and* TITANIA, *the Queen, at
another with hers*

OBERON   Ill met by moonlight, proud Titania!   60
TITANIA   What, jealous Oberon? Fairy, skip hence.
        I have forsworn his bed and company.
OBERON   Tarry, rash wanton! Am not I thy lord?
TITANIA   Then I must be thy lady. But I know
        When thou hast stol'n away from Fairyland
        And in the shape of Corin sat all day
        Playing on pipes of corn, and versing love
        To amorous Phillida. Why art thou here
        Come from the farthest steep of India
        But that, forsooth, the bouncing Amazon,   70
        Your buskined mistress and your warrior love,
        To Theseus must be wedded, and you come
        To give their bed joy and prosperity?
OBERON   How canst thou thus, for shame, Titania,
        Glance at my credit with Hippolyta,
        Knowing I know thy love to Theseus?
        Didst thou not lead him through the glimmering
          night
        From Perigenia, whom he ravishèd,
        And make him with fair Aegles break his faith,
        With Ariadne, and Antiopa?   80
TITANIA   These are the forgeries of jealousy;
        And never since the middle summer's spring
        Met we on hill, in dale, forest, or mead,
        By pavèd fountain or by rushy brook,
        Or in the beachèd margent of the sea
        To dance our ringlets to the whistling wind,
        But with thy brawls thou hast disturbed our
          sport.
        Therefore the winds, piping to us in vain,
        As in revenge, have sucked up from the sea
        Contagious fogs which, falling in the land,   90

80   Ariadne *the daughter of King Minos, who fell in love with Theseus and helped him to enter the labyrinth and kill the Minotaur and escape by means of a thread which she gave him. She fled with him and he deserted her on the Isle of Naxos.*

        Antiopa *an Amazon whom Theseus took prisoner in some versions of the legend. In others she is identified with Hippolyta.*

81–117   These are . . . original *For comment on these lines, see Introduction, p. 14.*

82   middle summer's spring *the beginning of mid-summer*

83   mead *meadow*

84   pavèd *with a layer of pebbles in the bottom*

85   in *on*

        margent *shore*

86   ringlets *dances performed in a ring with joined hands* to *to the sound of*

90   Contagious *pestilential, harmfu*

91   pelting *paltry, insignificant*

92   overborne *overflowed*

        continents *banks*

94   lost his sweat *i.e. because his labour produced no crops*

95   his *its*

        attained a beard *developed the 'beard' which grows on ripening corn*

97   murrion flock *cattle and sheep killed with the disease called 'murrain'*

98   nine men's morris *an area of grass marked out in squares in which two players perform a kind of open-air game of draughts using nine pieces or 'men' each. It was a popular rural summer game.*

99   quaint mazes *intricate wandering paths usually clearly visible owing to the constant running along them by the players of the game.*

        wanton green *luxuriant grass*

101   want *lack, are deprived of*

103   Therefore *This repeats the 'Therefore' in l. 88.*

        floods *tides*

104   washes *moistens, wets*

105   That *So that*

        rheumatic *i.e. those illnesses thought to be character-ised by the defluxion of 'rheum' (the moist secretions of the body), e.g. colds, coughs. The accent is on the first syllable.*

Hath every pelting river made so proud
That they have overborne their continents.
The ox hath therefore stretched his yoke in
    vain,
The ploughman lost his sweat, and the green
    corn
Hath rotted ere his youth attained a beard.
The fold stands empty in the drownèd field,
And crows are fatted with the murrion flock.
The nine men's morris is filled up with mud,
And the quaint mazes in the wanton green
For lack of tread are undistinguishable.   100
The human mortals want their winter cheer;
No night is now with hymn or carol blest.
Therefore the moon, the governess of floods,
Pale in her anger, washes all the air,
That rheumatic diseases do abound;
And thorough this distemperature we see
The seasons alter; hoary-headed frosts
Fall in the fresh lap of the crimson rose,
And on old Hiems' thin and icy crown
An odorus chaplet of sweet summer buds   110
Is as in mockery set. The spring, the summer,
The childing autumn, angry winter change
Their wonted liveries, and the mazèd world
By their increase now knows not which is which.
And this same progeny of evils comes
From our debate, from our dissension;
We are their parents and original.
OBERON Do you amend it then! It lies in you.
Why should Titania cross her Oberon?
I do but beg a little changeling boy   120
To be my henchman.
TITANIA   Set your heart at rest.
The fairy land buys not the child of me.
His mother was a vot'ress of my order,
And in the spicèd Indian air by night

106   thorough *through*

distemperature *There are two meanings possible here:
'the ill-humour of Titania and Oberon' and 'the bad
weather'.*

109   Hiems *a personification of winter*

110   chaplet *a wreath for the head*

112   childing *fruitful, productive*

change *exchange*

113   wonted liveries *customary clothing*

mazèd *bewildered*

114   increase *seasonal products*

115   progeny of evils *evil results*

116   debate *quarrel*

117   original *origin*

118   lies in *rests with*

119   cross *flouts the desire of*

120   changeling *Pronounced here with two syllables.*

121   henchman *page*

123   vot'ress of my order *one who had taken the vow in an
order of which Titania was the patroness*

127   traders *merchant ships*

flood *flood-tide*

128–9   conceive ... wind *Titania compares the sails of the
ship, filled out by the wind, with the swelling stomach
of a pregnant woman; see lines 130–32.*

129   wanton *sportive amorous*

131   squire *boy*

135   of that ... die *died in childbirth*

138   stay *This is the noun object of 'intend'.*

139   Perchance *Perhaps*

140   round *a dance performed in a circle*

142   spare *avoid, shun*

145   chide *quarrel*

downright *directly, outright*

146   not from *not go from*

147   injury *insult*

149   Since *When*

promontory *headland*

151   dulcet *sweet-sounding*

breath *voice, song*

152   rude *rough*

civil *calm, quiet*

156   cold *i.e. without heat; but also 'chaste' because per-
sonified by Diana*

Full often hath she gossiped by my side,
And sat with me on Neptune's yellow sands,
Marking th' embarkèd traders on the flood,
When we have laughed to see the sails conceive
And grow big-bellied with the wanton wind;
Which she, with pretty and with swimming gait 130
Following – her womb then rich with my young
    squire –
Would imitate, and sail upon the land
To fetch me trifles, and return again
As from a voyage, rich with merchandise.
But she, being mortal, of that boy did die,
And for her sake do I rear up her boy;
And for her sake I will not part with him.

OBERON How long within this wood intend you stay?

TITANIA Perchance till after Theseus' wedding day.
    If you will patiently dance in our round   140
    And see our moonlight revels, go with us.
    If not, shun me, and I will spare your haunts.

OBERON Give me that boy, and I will go with thee.

TITANIA Not for thy fairy kingdom! Fairies, away!
    We shall chide downright if I longer stay.

                  [*Exeunt* TITANIA *and her Train*

OBERON Well, go thy way. Thou shalt not from this
    grove
Till I torment thee for this injury.
My gentle Puck, come hither. Thou
    rememb'rest
Since once I sat upon a promontory
And heard a mermaid on a dolphin's back   150
Uttering such dulcet and harmonious breath
That the rude sea grew civil at her song,
And certain stars shot madly from their spheres
To hear the sea-maid's music.

PUCK   I remember.

OBERON That very time I saw – but thou couldst not –
Flying between the cold moon and the earth,

157   armed *i.e. with his bow and arrows*
            certain *accurate, sure*
158   fair vestal *beautiful virgin. This is usually taken to be a flattering allusion to Queen Elizabeth's imperial maidenhood.*
158   by *in*
159   love-shaft *i.e. Cupid's golden arrow*
161   might *could*
            fiery *because it produces the fires of passion*
163   imperial *majestic, queenly*
            vot'ress *of Diana's order, because a virgin*
164   fancy-free *free of love*
165   bolt *arrow*

168   love-in-idleness *pansy or heart's ease. This imaginary transformation may have been suggested to Shakespeare by Ovid's account of how Pyramus's blood turned the mulberry from white to purple.*

171   or . . . or *either . . . or*

174   leviathan *sea-monster; identified by the Elizabethans as a whale*

176–87   Having . . . conference *This is a direct address to the audience.*

181   busy *mischievous, meddlesome*

183   ere *before*

187   conference *conversation*

62

Cupid all armed. A certain aim he took
At a fair vestal thronèd by the west,
And loosed his love-shaft smartly from his
    bow
As it should pierce a hundred thousand hearts; 160
But I might see young Cupid's fiery shaft
Quenched in the chaste beams of the wat'ry
    moon,
And the imperial vot'ress passèd on,
In maiden meditation, fancy-free.
Yet marked I where the bolt of Cupid fell:
It fell upon a little western flower,
Before milk-white, now purple with love's
    wound,
And maidens call it 'love-in-idleness'.
Fetch me that flower – the herb I showed thee
    once.
The juice of it on sleeping eyelids laid   170
Will make or man or woman madly dote
Upon the next live creature that it sees.
Fetch me this herb, and be thou here again
Ere the leviathan can swim a league.

PUCK I'll put a girdle round about the earth
    In forty minutes!

                                [*Exit*

OBERON   Having once this juice,
    I'll watch Titania when she is asleep
And drop the liquor of it in her eyes.
The next thing then she, waking, looks upon –
Be it on lion, bear, or wolf, or bull,   180
On meddling monkey or on busy ape –
She shall pursue it with the soul of love.
And ere I take this charm from off her sight –
As I can take it with another herb –
I'll make her render up her page to me.
But who comes here? I am invisible,
And I will overhear their conference.

190   the other slayeth me *i.e. Hermia for whose love I am
          dying*

192   wood *mad*

195   adamant *iron-hard stone supposed to have magnetic
          properties*

196–8   But yet . . . steel *This is an extremely forced conceit.
          Helena appears to mean that although it is normal
          for the magnet to draw iron, in the case of the
          adamantine Demetrius he is drawing her heart to
          him, even though her heart is like steel in its truth.*

197   Leave you *Divest yourself of*

199   speak you fair *address you with kind words*

204   The more . . . you *The more you beat me the more I
          will fawn on you. Shakespeare frequently uses the
          spaniel as an image of fawning servility.*

210   used *treated*

214   impeach your modesty *cause your modesty to be sus-
          pect*

215   To leave *by leaving*

218   ill counsel *wicked prompting*
          desert *uninhabited*

64

Enter DEMETRIUS, HELENA *following him*

DEMETRIUS I love thee not, therefore pursue me not.
Where is Lysander and fair Hermia?
The one I'll slay, the other slayeth me. 190
Thou told'st me they were stol'n unto this
        wood,
And here am I, and wood within this wood
Because I cannot meet my Hermia.
Hence, get thee gone, and follow me no more!

HELENA You draw me, you hard-hearted adamant!
But yet you draw not iron; for my heart
Is true as steel. Leave you your power to draw,
And I shall have no power to follow you.

DEMETRIUS Do I entice you? Do I speak you fair?
Or rather do I not in plainest truth 200
Tell you I do not nor I cannot love you?

HELENA And even for that do I love you the more.
I am your spaniel; and, Demetrius,
The more you beat me I will fawn on you.
Use me but as your spaniel – spurn me, strike
        me,
Neglect me, lose me; only give me leave,
Unworthy as I am, to follow you.
What worser place can I beg in your love –
And yet a place of high respect with me –
Than to be usèd as you use your dog? 210

DEMETRIUS Tempt not too much the hatred of my
        spirit;
For I am sick when I do look on thee.

HELENA And I am sick when I look not on you.

DEMETRIUS You do impeach your modesty too much
To leave the city and commit yourself
Into the hands of one that loves you not,
To trust the opportunity of night
And the ill counsel of a desert place
With the rich worth of your virginity.

65

220   Your . . . privilege *There are several possible meanings
        here: (1) your transcendent attractions give me a
        special right to come; (2) your qualities change the
        normal circumstances (by making night into day)
        and therefore are a warrant of safety to me; (3) your
        moral goodness ensures my immunity from danger.*

220   For that *Because*

224   in my respect *in my regard*

227   brakes *thickets*

231   Apollo . . . chase *In the story as told by Ovid, Daphne
        in order to escape the amorous attentions of Apollo
        was changed into a laurel tree.*

232   griffin *a fabulous monster with the head and wings of an
        eagle and the body of a lion*
        hind *female deer*

233   bootless *useless*

235   stay thy *wait for thy*
        questions *reproachful conversation*

237   But *But that*
        do thee mischief *kill thee*

240   Your wrongs . . . set *the ill treatment you accord me
        causes me to behave in a way which is shameful in a
        woman*

244   To die *By dying*
        upon *by*

245   Oberon *He has been witnessing the exchange between
        Demetrius and Helena since l. 186 and here comes
        forward.*

HELENA Your virtue is my privilege. For that   220
        It is not night when I do see your face,
        Therefore I think I am not in the night;
        Nor doth this wood lack worlds of company,
        For you in my respect are all the world.
        Then how can it be said I am alone
        When all the world is here to look on me?

DEMETRIUS I'll run from thee and hide me in the brakes,
        And leave thee to the mercy of wild beasts.

HELENA The wildest hath not such a heart as you.
        Run when you will. The story shall be changed: 230
        Apollo flies and Daphne holds the chase,
        The dove pursues the griffin; the mild hind
        Makes speed to catch the tiger – bootless speed,
        When cowardice pursues, and valour flies.

DEMETRIUS I will not stay thy questions. Let me go!
        Or if thou follow me, do not believe
        But I shall do thee mischief in the wood.

HELENA Ay – in the temple, in the town, the field,
        You do me mischief. Fie, Demetrius!
        Your wrongs do set a scandal on my sex.   240
        We cannot fight for love, as men may do;
        We should be wooed, and were not made to
          woo.

                              [*Exit* DEMETRIUS

        I'll follow thee, and make a heaven of hell,
        To die upon the hand I love so well.

                                          [*Exit*

OBERON Fare thee well, nymph. Ere he do leave this
          grove,
        Thou shalt fly him, and he shall seek thy love.

                        Enter PUCK

        Hast thou the flower there? Welcome,
          wanderer.

PUCK Ay, there it is.

OBERON   I pray thee give it me.

250   blows *blossoms*

251   oxlips *a flowering herb, larger in form but of the same genus as the cowslip*

        grows *In Elizabethan grammar a singular verb form was often used when preceded by a compound subject.*

252   woodbine *honeysuckle*

253   musk-roses *wild roses*

        eglantine *sweet-brier*

254   sometime *for some period, during some part*

256   throws *sheds, casts*

257   Weed *Garment*

258   streak *anoint, smear*

259   fantasies *fancies*

266   prove *turn out to be*

267   fond on *infatuated with*

268   ere *before*

        first cockcrow *i.e. the coming of dawn, a time which caused certain supernatural beings to take flight. However, Oberon deliberately dissociates himself from this limitation at III. 2. 395.*

ACT TWO, scene 2

The location of the scene is the bank described by Oberon at II. 1. 250–55. On the Elizabethan stage no change of place would be indicated. Possibly the main acting area was used for the Lysander–Hermia–Helena exchanges in lines 41–162, with Titania's bower being some kind of enclosure at the rear or to one side of the stage. The scene involves the Fairies actively in the affairs of the Lovers, and shows the prosecution of Oberon's plan for revenge on Titania.

1   roundel *a dance performed with the dancers holding hands in a circle*

2   third part of a minute *In accordance with the reduced scale of the Fairies, Shakespeare here scales down the time they take to perform actions.*

3   cankers *small worms that attack the centre of roses*

        musk-rose *a large white rose*

4   reremice *bats*

7   quaint *daintily or prettily fashioned*

8   to your offices *go about your various duties*

I know a bank where the wild thyme blows,   250
Where oxlips and the nodding violet grows,
Quite overcanopied with luscious woodbine,
With sweet musk-roses, and with eglantine.
There sleeps Titania sometime of the night,
Lulled in these flowers with dances and delight.
And there the snake throws her enamelled skin,
Weed wide enough to wrap a fairy in.
And with the juice of this I'll streak her eyes
And make her full of hateful fantasies.
Take thou some of it, and seek through this
    grove.   260
A sweet Athenian lady is in love
With a disdainful youth – anoint his eyes;
But do it when the next thing he espies
May be the lady. Thou shalt know the man
By the Athenian garments he hath on.
Effect it with some care, that he may prove
More fond on her than she upon her love.
And look thou meet me ere the first cock crow.

PUCK Fear not, my lord; your servant shall do so.
                                  [Exeunt

Scene 2. *Enter* TITANIA, *Queen of Fairies, with her Train*

TITANIA Come, now a roundel and a fairy song;
Then for the third part of a minute, hence –
Some to kill cankers in the musk-rose buds,
Some war with reremice for their leathern
    wings
To make my small elves coats, and some keep
    back
The clamorous owl that nightly hoots and
    wonders
At our quaint spirits. Sing me now asleep.
Then to your offices, and let me rest.

FAIRIES *sing*

9   double *forked*

10   thorny *with quills*

11   blindworms *small harmless snakes. Both these and newts were considered in Shakespeare's time to be venomous and were often connected with spells and witches; compare* Macbeth, *IV. 1 where the Witches' cauldron contains 'eye of a newt' and 'blindworm's sting'.*

13   Philomel *a name for the nightingale derived from the girl in Greek mythology who was changed into this bird*

18   Come . . . nigh *approach, draw near*

20   spiders *These were considered poisonous in Shakespeare's time; compare* Richard II, *III. 2. 14 'spiders that suck up venom'.*

32   One . . . sentinel *Most Elizabethan stages had some kind of upper acting area or balcony. Possibly one of Titania's attendants was intended to stand guard there ('aloof'), and would thus miss Oberon's entry on the lower stage at l. 33. In modern productions the sentinel is sometimes played by a boy who is comically overpowered by Oberon's attendants.*

33–40   What thou . . . near *This is an example of the four-stress verse which Shakespeare employs to characterise the fairy world of the play. See the Introduction, p. 15 where the variations of the verse are discussed.*

36   ounce *lynx*

         cat *Presumably a wild rather than a domesticated cat is intended here.*

70

FIRST FAIRY   You spotted snakes with double tongue,
            Thorny hedgehogs, be not seen;   10
        Newts and blindworms, do no wrong,
            Come not near our Fairy Queen.

CHORUS   Philomel, with melody
            Sing in our sweet lullaby,
      Lulla, lulla, lullaby; lulla, lulla, lullaby.
              Never harm
             Nor spell nor charm
           Come our lovely lady nigh.
           So good night, with lullaby.

FIRST FAIRY   Weaving spiders, come not here: 20
            Hence, you long-legged spinners, hence!
        Beetles black, approach not near,
            Worm nor snail, do no offence.

CHORUS   Philomel, with melody
            Sing in our sweet lullaby,
      Lulla, lulla, lullaby; lulla, lulla, lullaby.
              Never harm
             Nor spell nor charm
           Come our lovely lady nigh.
           So good night, with lullaby.   30
                   [TITANIA *sleeps*

SECOND FAIRY   Hence, away! Now all is well.
            One aloof stand sentinel.
                 [*Exeunt* FAIRIES

Enter OBERON *and squeezes the flower juice on*
             TITANIA's *eyelids*

OBERON   What thou seest when thou dost wake,
            Do it for thy true-love take;
            Love and languish for his sake.
            Be it ounce or cat or bear,

37   Pard *Leopard*

42   troth *truth*

44   And tarry . . . day *And wait until daylight can help us*

48   troth *faith pledged by lovers*

51–2   O, take . . . conference *O, understand the real meaning of my innocent remark. In conversation between lovers, their love should enable them to understand each other truly.*
53   knit *joined inextricably*
55   interchainèd with *bound together by*
56   a single troth *one pledged love*
58   lying so *Lysander, in modern productions, often attempts to lie down close to Hermia's side at this point.*
        lie *deceive (with a pun on the sense 'lie down')*
59   riddles *plays on words*
        prettily *cleverly, neatly*
60   beshrew *literally 'curse', but, as here, the word could be used lightly.*
61   lied *told a lie (taking up Lysander's pun in l. 58)*
63   human modesty *Hermia's appeal is to Lysander's sense of civilised decorum.*
66   so far be distant *In modern productions this is sometimes played as an indication that Lysander has gone too far away for Hermia's comfort.*
67–9   Thy love . . . loyalty *This stress is made so that Lysander's later desertion induced by Puck's love potion may be the more dramatically striking.*

72

Pard, or boar with bristled hair,
In thy eye that shall appear
When thou wak'st, it is thy dear:
Wake when some vile thing is near! 40

[*Exit*

Enter LYSANDER *and* HERMIA

LYSANDER Fair love, you faint with wand'ring in the
wood;
And – to speak troth – I have forgot our way.
We'll rest us, Hermia, if you think it good,
And tarry for the comfort of the day.
HERMIA Be it so, Lysander; find you out a bed,
For I upon this bank will rest my head.
LYSANDER One turf shall serve as pillow for us
both;
One heart, one bed, two bosoms, and one troth.
HERMIA Nay, good Lysander; for my sake, my dear,
Lie further off yet; do not lie so near. 50
LYSANDER O, take the sense, sweet, of my innocence!
Love takes the meaning in love's conference –
I mean that my heart unto yours is knit,
So that but one heart we can make of it;
Two bosoms interchainèd with an oath –
So then two bosoms and a single troth.
Then by your side no bed-room me deny,
For lying so, Hermia, I do not lie.
HERMIA Lysander riddles very prettily.
Now much beshrew my manners and my pride 60
If Hermia meant to say Lysander lied.
But, gentle friend, for love and courtesy
Lie further off, in human modesty:
Such separation as may well be said
Becomes a virtuous bachelor and a maid,
So far be distant, and good night, sweet friend;
Thy love ne'er alter till thy sweet life end.
LYSANDER Amen, amen, to that fair prayer say I,

71   With half ... pressed *i.e. may your eyelids be pressed down in sleep with half the restful slumber you have wished me*

74   approve *test, try out*

76   Who is here? *Puck here mistakes Lysander for Demetrius.*

77   Weeds *Garments*

78   he my master *he that my master*

83   kill-courtesy *one who destroys courtesy with churlishness*

84   Churl *Boor, one who lacks manners*

85   owe *possess*

86–7   let love ... eyelid *may love make you sleepless; this was considered a common symptom of the young lover.*

91   haunt *follow persistently*

92   darkling *in darkness. This is a typical verbal indication of night which could not otherwise be represented in the Elizabethan open-air theatres.*

And then end life when I end loyalty.
Here is my bed. Sleep give thee all his rest!　70

HERMIA With half that wish the wisher's eyes be
pressed.

[They sleep

Enter PUCK

PUCK　　Through the forest have I gone,
But Athenian found I none
On whose eyes I might approve
This flower's force in stirring love.
Night and silence – Who is here?
Weeds of Athens he doth wear.
This is he my master said
Despisèd the Athenian maid;
And here the maiden, sleeping sound　80
On the dank and dirty ground.
Pretty soul, she durst not lie
Near this lack-love, this kill-courtesy.
Churl, upon thy eyes I throw
All the power this charm doth owe.
When thou wak'st, let love forbid
Sleep his seat on thy eyelid.

He squeezes the flower juice on LYSANDER'S *eyelids*
So, awake when I am gone;
For I must now to Oberon.

[Exit

Enter DEMETRIUS *and* HELENA, *running*

HELENA Stay, though thou kill me, sweet
Demetrius!　90

DEMETRIUS I charge thee hence; and do not haunt me
thus.

HELENA O, wilt thou darkling leave me?
Do not so!

DEMETRIUS Stay, on thy peril! I alone will go.

[Exit

94   fond *foolishly doting*

95   the lesser . . . grace *the less is my prayer answered*

104   glass *mirror*

105   sphery eyne *eyes as bright as stars*

110   Transparent *Lysander uses the word in its sense of 'brilliant, glorious', but in ll. 110–11 he uses the word in another sense: 'ingenuous, able to be seen through'.*
         art *magical power*

112   fit *appropriate*

115   What though *What does it matter that*

116   content *happy. Lysander shifts the meaning in the following line to 'satisfied with'.*

120   raven for a dove *From this and other indications in the text (e.g. III. 2. 188 and 259) Shakespeare conceived Helena as fair and Hermia as dark in hair and complexion.*

121   The will . . . swayed *Lysander believes that it is his reason that has made him favour Helena not Puck's love potion; see Introduction, p. 11.*
         will *desire*

124   ripe not to reason *did not mature in my full powers of reason*

125   And touching . . . skill *And now that I have achieved the fullness of human understanding*

126   will *desire*

HELENA   O, I am out of breath in this fond chase.
         The more my prayer, the lesser is my grace.
         Happy is Hermia, whereso'er she lies,
         For she hath blessèd and attractive eyes.
         How came her eyes so bright? Not with salt
            tears –
         If so, my eyes are oft'ner washed than hers.
         No, no – I am as ugly as a bear,   100
         For beasts that meet me run away for fear.
         Therefore no marvel though Demetrius
         Do as a monster fly my presence thus.
         What wicked and dissembling glass of mine
         Made me compare with Hermia's sphery eyne?
         But who is here? – Lysander on the ground?
         Dead – or asleep? I see no blood, no wound.
         Lysander, if you live, good sir, awake!

LYSANDER [*Awaking*] And run through fire I will for
            thy sweet sake.
         Transparent Helena, Nature shows art,   110
         That through thy bosom makes me see thy
            heart.
         Where is Demetrius? O, how fit a word
         Is that vile name to perish on my sword!

HELENA   Do not say so, Lysander, say not so.
         What though he love your Hermia? Lord! What
            though?
         Yet Hermia still loves you. Then be content.

LYSANDER Content with Hermia? No, I do repent
         The tedious minutes I with her have spent.
         Not Hermia but Helena I love;
         Who will not change a raven for a dove?   120
         The will of man is by his reason swayed,
         And reason says you are the worthier maid.
         Things growing are not ripe until their season;
         So I, being young, till now ripe not to reason.
         And touching now the point of human skill,
         Reason becomes the marshal to my will

127   o'erlook *read over*

129   Wherefore *Why*

133   Deserve *Merit, earn*
134   flout *jeer at*
       insufficiency *lack of ability to attract men*
135   Good troth *indeed*
       good sooth *in truth, really. This expletive lends more
          force to the assertion than the earlier milder expletive
          'Good troth'.*
138   gentleness *good breeding, courtesy*
139   of *by*

143   surfeit *overdose*

145–6 as the heresies ... deceive *as the heresies that men
          reject are detested most by the very men who were
          misled by them*

148   of *by*
149   address *direct, apply*

150   knight *true lover and servant*

156   prey *the act of preying*

And leads me to your eyes, where I o'erlook
Love's stories written in Love's richest book.

HELENA Wherefore was I to this keen mockery born?
When at your hands did I deserve this scorn?   130
Is't not enough, is't not enough, young man,
That I did never – no, nor never can –
Deserve a sweet look from Demetrius' eye
But you must flout my insufficiency?
Good troth, you do me wrong – good sooth,
    you do –
In such disdainful manner me to woo.
But fare you well. Perforce I must confess
I thought you lord of more true gentleness.
O, that a lady of one man refused
Should of another therefore be abused!   140
                                                        [Exit

LYSANDER She sees not Hermia. Hermia, sleep thou
    there,
And never mayst thou come Lysander near.
For, as a surfeit of the sweetest things
The deepest loathing to the stomach brings,
Or as the heresies that men do leave
Are hated most of those they did deceive,
So thou, my surfeit and my heresy,
Of all be hated, but the most of me!
And, all my powers, address your love and
    might
To honour Helen and to be her knight.   150
                                                        [Exit

HERMIA [Awaking suddenly] Help me, Lysander, help
    me! do thy best
To pluck this crawling serpent from my breast!
Ay me, for pity! – What a dream was here!
Lysander, look how I do quake with fear!
Methought a serpent ate my heart away,
And you sat smiling at his cruel prey.
Lysander! What, removed? Lysander, lord!

159   an if *if*
160   of all loves *by all true loves*
161   nigh *close by*

What, out of hearing? Gone? No sound, no
    word?
Alack, where are you? Speak, an if you hear.
Speak, of all loves! I swoon almost with fear. 160
No? Then I well perceive you are not nigh.
Either death or you I'll find immediately.

                                    [Exit

ACT THREE, scene 1

On the Elizabethan stage there would be no break between the preceding scene and this one; Hermia would merely exit through one door and the artisans would enter through another. The scene shows the involvement of Bottom with Titania, which is by implication a grotesque version of the other love affairs in the play, and thus the furtherance of Oberon's revenge plot.

	clowns *rustics*
2	Pat *On the dot, punctually*
4	hawthorn brake *hawthorn thicket. Hawthorn branches were used in May Day love rituals.*
	tiring-house *In the Elizabethan theatre the tiring-house or dressing-room was located immediately behind the back wall of the stage to which Bottom would presumably gesture as the 'hawthorn brake'.*
7	bully *good fellow*
11	abide *bear, endure*
12	By'r lakin *By Our Lady (a mild oath)*
	parlous *terrible, dangerous*
14	when all is done *after all*
15	Not a whit *Not at all*
16	Write me *Write (a colloquialism)*
	seem to say *say as he acts his rôle*
18–19	more better *The double comparative was a common grammatical construction and is not here a sign of Bottom's ignorance.*
23	in eight and six *in alternating lines of eight and six syllables (a common ballad metre)*
29	yourself *One of the earliest editions of the play has 'yourselves' here but this singular form may be deliberate on Shakespeare's part as another indication of Bottom's ignorance.*

ACT THREE

Scene 1. *Enter the clowns:* QUINCE, BOTTOM, SNUG, FLUTE, SNOUT, *and* STARVELING

BOTTOM Are we all met?

QUINCE Pat, pat; and here's a marvellous convenient place for our rehearsal. This green plot shall be our stage, this hawthorn brake our tiring-house, and we will do it in action as we will do it before the Duke.

BOTTOM Peter Quince!

QUINCE What sayest thou, bully Bottom?

BOTTOM There are things in this comedy of Pyramus and Thisbe that will never please. First, Pyramus must draw a sword to kill himself, which the ladies 10 cannot abide. How answer you that?

SNOUT By 'r lakin, a parlous fear!

STARVELING I believe we must leave the killing out, when all is done.

BOTTOM Not a whit. I have a device to make all well. Write me a prologue, and let the prologue seem to say we will do no harm with our swords, and that Pyramus is not killed indeed; and for the more better assurance, tell them that I, Pyramus, am not Pyramus, but Bottom the weaver. This will put them 20 out of fear.

QUINCE Well, we will have such a prologue, and it shall be written in eight and six.

BOTTOM No, make it two more; let it be written in eight and eight.

SNOUT Will not the ladies be afeard of the lion?

STARVELING I fear it, I promise you.

BOTTOM Masters, you ought to consider with yourself: to bring in – God shield us! – a lion among ladies is a most dreadful thing; for there is not a 30 more fearful wild-fowl than your lion living; and we ought to look to 't.

38   defect *Bottom's mistake for 'effect'*

41–2   were pity of my life *i.e. my life would be in danger (of execution)*

47   *In one early text of the play Puck enters at this point which may indicate that it was a contemporary stage practice to have Puck witness the doings of the mechanicals before he speaks at l. 74.*

54   casement *hinged window*

55   Great Chamber *the State Room of the ducal palace*

57–8   One must . . . lantern *These were traditional symbols of the man in the moon and are referred to by Ben Jonson as 'stale ensigns of the stage's man in the moon'.*

                  bush of thorns *bundle of sticks, which was a common symbol of the man in the moon. The allusion is often taken to be to the man who gathered firewood on the Sabbath in Numbers XV: 32–6.*

58   disfigure *Bottom's mistake for 'figure' (symbolise)*

59   present *represent*

64   present *represent*

66   roughcast *a mixture of lime and gravel used to plaster over the outside walls of houses*

84

SNOUT   Therefore another prologue must tell he is
not a lion.

BOTTOM   Nay, you must name his name, and half his
face must be seen through the lion's neck, and he
himself must speak through, saying thus, or to the
same defect: 'Ladies', or 'Fair ladies – I would
wish you' or 'I would request you' or 'I would
entreat you – not to fear, not to tremble. My life for   40
yours: if you think I come hither as a lion, it were
pity of my life. No, I am no such thing. I am a man
as other men are.' – And there indeed let him name
his name, and tell them plainly he is Snug the joiner.

QUINCE   Well, it shall be so. But there is two hard
things: that is, to bring the moonlight into a chamber – for, you know, Pyramus and Thisbe meet by
moonlight.

SNUG   Doth the moon shine that night we play our
play?   50

BOTTOM   A calendar, a calendar! Look in the almanac –
find out moonshine, find out moonshine!

QUINCE   Yes, it doth shine that night.

BOTTOM   Why, then may you leave a casement of the
Great Chamber window – where we play – open,
and the moon may shine in at the casement.

QUINCE   Ay; or else one must come in with a bush of
thorns and a lantern, and say he comes to disfigure,
or to present, the person of Moonshine. Then there
is another thing. We must have a wall in the Great   60
Chamber; for Pyramus and Thisbe, says the story,
did talk through the chink of a wall.

SNOUT   You can never bring in a wall. What say you,
Bottom?

BOTTOM   Some man or other must present Wall; and
let him have some plaster, or some loam, or some
roughcast about him to signify Wall; and let him
hold his fingers thus, and through that cranny shall
Pyramus and Thisbe whisper.

71 every mother's son *every one of you*
  rehearse *run through, go over*

73 brake *thicket*

75 hempen homespuns *men dressed in coarse cloth spun from hemp*

77 toward *in preparation*

79–82 Thisbe ... dear *The intention of this passage is not clear owing to some confusion in the early texts. The possibilities are (1) that Bottom pronounces 'have' as 'of' and that Quince corrects 'odious' to 'odorous'; (2) that Quince corrects 'odious' to 'odours' and that the second line in the quotation is the kind of non-sequence of thought that typifies the speeches of the playlet.*

85 A stranger ... here *The idea for the transformation of Bottom occurs to Puck at this point.*

92 brisky *brisk*
  juvenal *youth*
  eke *also; a deliberate archaism by Shakespeare*
  Jew *This has been variously explained as an abbreviation of 'jewel' or 'juvenile'. However, in this context it probably is introduced by Shakespeare for the sake of humorous incongruity.*

94 Ninny *Fool*

95 Ninus' tomb *The meeting place of Thisbe and Pyramus according to Ovid's version of the legend. Ninus was the husband of Semiramis and the legendary founder of Nineveh.*

96–7 You speak ... and all *This was a good deal more easily done in Shakespeare's day than now. An individual player's part (i.e. his lines and cues) were written on a narrow continuous roll of paper wound on wooden rollers at each end.*

86

QUINCE If that may be, then all is well. Come, sit   70
down every mother's son, and rehearse your parts.
Pyramus, you begin. When you have spoken your
speech, enter into that brake; and so every one
according to his cue.

Enter PUCK

PUCK What hempen homespuns have we swagg'ring
here,
So near the cradle of the Fairy Queen?
What, a play toward? I'll be an auditor;
An actor too perhaps, if I see cause.
QUINCE Speak, Pyramus! Thisbe, stand forth!
BOTTOM as Pyramus *Thisbe, the flowers of odious*
savours sweet —
QUINCE Odours — odours!   80
BOTTOM as Pyramus *— odours savours sweet;*
So hath thy breath, my dearest Thisbe dear.
But hark, a voice! Stay thou but here awhile,
And by and by I will to thee appear.
PUCK A stranger Pyramus than e'er played here!
[*Exit*

FLUTE Must I speak now?
QUINCE Ay, marry must you; for you must under-
stand he goes but to see a noise that he heard, and is
to come again.
FLUTE as Thisbe *Most radiant Pyramus, most lily-*
white of hue,   90
Of colour like the red rose on triumphant brier,
Most brisky juvenal, and eke most lovely Jew,
As true as truest horse that yet would never tire,
I'll meet thee, Pyramus, at Ninny's tomb —
QUINCE 'Ninus' tomb', man! Why, you must not
speak that yet. That you answer to Pyramus. You
speak all your part at once, cues and all. Pyramus,
enter — your cue is past. It is 'never tire.'

101 fair *handsome*
     were *would be*

104 about a round *roundabout*
105 Thorough *Through*

107 headless *Figures without heads have long been associated with ghostly happenings.*
     fire *will-o'-the-wisp*

110 knavery *knavish trick*

114–15 You see ... own *Bottom means that Snout sees a reflection of his own stupid brain.*

117 translated *transformed; a regular Elizabethan meaning of the word, thus not a malapropism.*

121 that *so that*

FLUTE O!

(as Thisbe) *As true as truest horse that yet would
never tire.* 100

Enter BOTTOM *with an ass-head, followed by*
PUCK

BOTTOM as Pyramus *If I were fair, Thisbe, I were only
thine.*

QUINCE O monstrous! O strange! We are haunted!
Pray, masters! Fly, masters! Help!

[*Exeunt* QUINCE, SNUG, FLUTE, SNOUT, *and* STARVELING

PUCK I'll follow you; I'll lead you about a round,
Thorough bog, thorough bush, thorough brake,
thorough brier.
Sometime a horse I'll be, sometime a hound,
A hog, a headless bear, sometime a fire;
And neigh, and bark, and grunt, and roar, and
burn,
Like horse, hound, hog, bear, fire, at every turn.

[*Exit*

BOTTOM Why do they run away? This is a knavery of 110
them to make me afeard.

Enter SNOUT

SNOUT O Bottom, thou art changed. What do I see
on thee?

BOTTOM What do you see? You see an ass-head of
your own, do you?

[*Exit* SNOUT

Enter QUINCE

QUINCE Bless thee, Bottom, bless thee! Thou art
translated. [*Exit*

BOTTOM I see their knavery. This is to make an ass of
me, to fright me, if they could; but I will not stir
from this place, do what they can. I will walk up 120
and down here, and will sing, that they shall hear I
am not afraid.

123   Sings *The birds in this song are a deliberate contrast with those in the song with which Titania was lulled to sleep in II. 2. 9 ff.*

123   ousel *blackbird*

124   orange-tawny *dark yellow*

125   throstle *thrush*

126   little quill *thin piping voice*

130   plain-song *unadorned song; the reference is to the repeated sound the bird makes.*

131   mark *take note of*

133   set his wit . . . bird *use his intelligence to answer such a stupid bird*

134   give a . . . lie *accuse of untruthfulness. The cuckoo was considered to be naming in its song the deceived husband or 'cuckold'.*

135   never so *ever so much*

137   note *melody*

139–40   And thy . . . me *And the power of your attractive personal qualities has persuaded me*

143–4   And yet . . . nowadays *See the Introduction, p. 13 for comment on this idea.*

146   gleek *make a satirical jest*

149   to serve . . . turn *to serve my purpose*

153   no common rate *no ordinary rank*

154   still *always*

    tend upon *wait upon (as part of her train)*

157   jewels . . . deep *Other precious stones, like pearls, were considered by the Elizabethans to come from the bed of the sea.*

Sings

    The ousel cock so black of hue,
        With orange-tawny bill,
    The throstle with his note so true,
        The wren with little quill, –

TITANIA [*Awaking*] What angel wakes me from my
    flow'ry bed?

BOTTOM   The finch, the sparrow, and the lark,
        The plain-song cuckoo grey,   130
    Whose note full many a man doth mark,
        And dares not answer nay –
for, indeed, who would set his wit to so foolish a
bird? Who would give a bird the lie, though he cry
'cuckoo' never so?

TITANIA I pray thee, gentle mortal, sing again!
    Mine ear is much enamoured of thy note.
    So is mine eye enthrallèd to thy shape;
    And thy fair virtue's force perforce doth move
      me   140
    On the first view, to say, to swear, I love thee.

BOTTOM Methinks, mistress, you should have little
reason for that. And yet, to say the truth, reason and
love keep little company together nowadays – the
more the pity that some honest neighbours will not
make them friends. – Nay, I can gleek upon occasion.

TITANIA Thou art as wise as thou art beautiful.

BOTTOM Not so, neither; but if I had wit enough to
get out of this wood, I have enough to serve mine
own turn.   150

TITANIA Out of this wood do not desire to go!
    Thou shalt remain here, whether thou wilt or
      no.
    I am a spirit of no common rate,
    The summer still doth tend upon my state,
    And I do love thee. Therefore go with me.
    I'll give thee fairies to attend on thee,
    And they shall fetch thee jewels from the deep,

161   Moth *This was a normal spelling of 'mote' meaning 'speck'. However, the connection of the name here with Cobweb may indicate that the modern 'moth' is intended. Both 'moth' and 'mote' were spelled 'moth' by the Elizabethans but were pronounced 'mote'.*

168   gambol *cavort playfully*

169   apricocks *an old form of 'apricots'*
        dewberries *a type of blackberry*

171   humble-bees *i.e. bumble-bees*

172   crop . . . thighs *i.e. trim the wax from their thighs*

173   light them . . . eyes *It has been pointed out that Shakespeare's natural history is at fault here in that the glow worm's light is in its tail.*

174   To have *To attend*

182   I cry . . . mercy *I beg your pardon (for having to ask your name)*

185   I shall . . . acquaintance *A common polite formula on being introduced to a stranger*

186   If . . . finger *Cobwebs were used to staunch bleeding*

187   make bold with you *undertake to use you*

And sing while thou on pressèd flowers dost
    sleep;
And I will purge thy mortal grossness so
That thou shalt like an airy spirit go.   160
Peaseblossom, Cobweb, Moth, and Mustard-
    seed!

Enter PEASEBLOSSOM, COBWEB, MOTH, *and*
MUSTARDSEED

PEASEBLOSSOM Ready!
COBWEB   And I!
MOTH   And I!
MUSTARDSEED And I!
ALL   Where shall we go?
TITANIA Be kind and courteous to this gentleman.
    Hop in his walks and gambol in his eyes;
    Feed him with apricocks and dewberries,
    With purple grapes, green figs, and mulberries. 170
    The honey-bags steal from the humble-bees,
    And for night-tapers crop their waxen thighs,
    And light them at the fiery glow-worm's eyes
    To have my love to bed and to arise;
    And pluck the wings from painted butterflies
    To fan the moonbeams from his sleeping eyes.
    Nod to him, elves, and do him courtesies.
PEASEBLOSSOM Hail, mortal!
COBWEB   Hail!
MOTH   Hail!   180
MUSTARDSEED Hail!
BOTTOM I cry your worships mercy, heartily, I
  beseech your worship's name.
COBWEB   Cobweb.
BOTTOM I shall desire you of more acquaintance,
  good Master Cobweb. If I cut my finger, I shall
  make bold with you! Your name, honest gentleman?
PEASEBLOSSOM Peaseblossom.

190   Squash *an unripe pea-pod*
         Peascod *a mature pea-pod*

196   patience *i.e. in being used so often in the eating of beef*
198–9   made my eyes water *Bottom means both that his eyes
              have watered from the strength of mustard and also
              that he has wept in sympathy with the lot of
              Mustardseed's 'kindred'.*
         ere *before*
203   when she weeps . . . flower *The moon was considered
              to be the cause of dew.*
204   enforcèd *violated*
         chastity *The reference is to Diana goddess of the moon
              and of chastity.*
205   Tie up . . . tongue *In modern productions it is common
              for Bottom to punctuate his speeches with a series of
              'hee-haws' after his entry wearing the ass's head.*

ACT THREE, scene 2

*There is no break in the action between this scene and III. 1.
However, the way in which Oberon's opening lines sum up
the earlier situation may indicate that an interval did take
place at this point in Elizabethan performances. The Lovers'
predicament in this scene is further complicated by the interference of Puck and Oberon; and it ends with the sorting
out of the couples in preparation for their awakening by
Theseus in IV. 1.*

3   in extremity *to excess*
5   night-rule *actions in the night with overtones of 'mis-
              rule'*
7   close *secret, private*
8   dull *drowsy*
9   patches *clowns, fools*
         rude mechanicals *rough labouring men*
13   shallowest *most stupid*
         barren sort *stupid crew*

94

BOTTOM   I pray you, commend me to Mistress
Squash, your mother, and to Master Peascod, your 190
father. Good Master Peaseblossom, I shall desire
you of more acquaintance too. Your name, I beseech
you, sir?

MUSTARDSEED   Mustardseed.

BOTTOM   Good Master Mustardseed, I know your
patience well. That same cowardly, giantlike
ox-beef hath devoured many a gentleman of your
house. I promise you, your kindred hath made my
eyes water ere now. I desire you of more acquaintance, good Master Mustardseed.   200

TITANIA   Come wait upon him; lead him to my bower.
The moon, methinks, looks with a wat'ry eye;
And when she weeps, weeps every little flower,
Lamenting some enforcèd chastity.
Tie up my lover's tongue, bring him silently.
                                             [*Exeunt*

Scene 2. *Enter* OBERON, *King of Fairies*

OBERON   I wonder if Titania be awaked;
Then what it was that next came in her eye,
Which she must dote on in extremity.
Here comes my messenger.

Enter PUCK

                        How now, mad spirit?
What night-rule now about this haunted grove?

PUCK   My mistress with a monster is in love.
Near to her close and consecrated bower,
While she was in her dull and sleeping hour,
A crew of patches, rude mechanicals
That work for bread upon Athenian stalls,   10
Were met together to rehearse a play
Intended for great Theseus' nuptial day.
The shallowest thickskin of that barren sort,

14   presented *represented, acted*

15   scene *stage, acting area*
       brake *thicket*

17   noll *head, noddle*

19   mimic *burlesque actor*

20   eye *perceive*

21   russet-pated choughs *grey-headed jackdaws*
       in sort *in a flock*

23   Sever *Separate*

24   his sight *the sight of him*

25   at our stamp *at the sound of my footsteps. Some scholars read this as an error for 'at our stump' (some special fairy tree stump known to Oberon).*

26   He *i.e. one of them*

28   senseless things *inanimate objects*
       wrong *injury*

30   From yielders . . . catch *This is a generalised observation: 'on those already vanquished all things prey'.*

32   translated *transformed*

36   latched *either 'fastened (in love)' or 'moistened'*

40   That *So that*
       of force *necessarily*
       eyed *viewed*

41   close *concealed*

44   Lay breath *Use language*

96

Who Pyramus presented in their sport,
Forsook his scene and entered in a brake.
When I did him at this advantage take,
An ass's noll I fixèd on his head.
Anon his Thisbe must be answerèd,
And forth my mimic comes. When they him
    spy –
As wild geese that the creeping fowler eye,   20
Or russet-pated choughs, many in sort,
Rising and cawing at the gun's report,
Sever themselves and madly sweep the sky –
So, at his sight, away his fellows fly,
And at our stamp here o'er and o'er one falls;
He 'Murder!' cries and help from Athens calls.
Their sense thus weak, lost with their fears thus
    strong,
Made senseless things begin to do them wrong;
For briers and thorns at their apparel snatch,
Some sleeves, some hats, from yielders all
    things catch.   30
I led them on in this distracted fear,
And left sweet Pyramus translated there;
When in that moment – so it came to pass –
Titania waked, and straightway loved an ass.

OBERON This falls out better than I could devise!
But hast thou yet latched the Athenian's eyes
With the love-juice, as I did bid thee do?

PUCK I took him sleeping – that is finished too;
And the Athenian woman by his side,
That when he waked, of force she must be
    eyed.   40

Enter DEMETRIUS *and* HERMIA

OBERON   Stand close. This is the same Athenian.
PUCK   This is the woman, but not this the man.
DEMETRIUS O, why rebuke you him that loves you so?
Lay breath so bitter on your bitter foe.

48   o'er shoes *so far gone*
       deep *the depths of guilt*

53-5   This whole . . . Antipodes *This solid earth's core may
       be tunnelled through, so that the moon may pass
       through the earth and will displease the noontime that
       the sun is bringing to those inhabitants who live on the
       other side of the globe.*

57   dead *deadly*

61   sphere *orbit; see note to II. 1. 7.*

70   O, brave touch *O, a fine strike (ironical)*

71   worm *snake*

72   doubler tongue *The allusion is to the forked tongue of
       the adder and to the greater deceitfulness of Deme-
       trius.*

98

HERMIA   Now I but chide; but I should use thee
        worse,
        For thou, I fear, hast given me cause to curse.
        If thou hast slain Lysander in his sleep,
        Being o'er shoes in blood, plunge in the deep,
        And kill me too.
        The sun was not so true unto the day   50
        As he to me. Would he have stol'n away
        From sleeping Hermia? I'll believe as soon
        This whole earth may be bored, and that the
          moon
        May through the centre creep, and so displease
        Her brother's noontide with th' Antipodes.
        It cannot be but thou hast murdered him.
        So should a murderer look – so dead, so grim.
DEMETRIUS So should the murdered look, and so
          should I,
        Pierced through the heart with your stern
          cruelty.
        Yet you, the murderer, look as bright, as clear,   60
        As yonder Venus in her glimmering sphere.
HERMIA   What's this to my Lysander? Where is
        he?
        Ah, good Demetrius, wilt thou give him me?
DEMETRIUS I had rather give his carcass to my hounds.
HERMIA   Out, dog! Out, cur! Thou driv'st me past
        the bounds
        Of maiden's patience. Hast thou slain him then?
        Henceforth be never numbered among men.
        O, once tell true – tell true, even for my sake.
        Durst thou have looked upon him, being
          awake?
        And hast thou killed him sleeping? O, brave
          touch!   70
        Could not a worm, an adder do so much?
        An adder did it; for with doubler tongue
        Than thine – thou serpent! – never adder stung.

74   spend your passion *waste your emotion*
      misprised mood *mistaken cause for anger*

78   An *Even*
      Therefore *For that*

81   whether *This could be pronounced 'whe'er'.*

82   fierce vein *wrathful mood*

84–5 So sorrow's . . . owe *Thus the sadness induced by*
      Sorrow causes the man who experiences it to become
      drowsier and in need of the healing rest that Sleep,
      like a bankrupt, cannot render him.
87   tender *offer*
      make some stay *wait a while*

90   Of thy misprision *From your mistake*

92–3 Then fate . . . oath *Therefore fate has exercised its*
      power so that for every one man who is faithful to his
      word a million are not in breaking vow after vow.

95   look *make sure*
96   fancy-sick *love-sick*
      cheer *countenance*
97   With sighs . . . dear *It was thought at this time that*
      every sigh cost the heart a drop of blood.

99   against *in preparation for when*

100

DEMETRIUS You spend your passion on a misprised
        mood.
      I am not guilty of Lysander's blood;
      Nor is he dead, for aught that I can tell.
HERMIA   I pray thee, tell me then that he is well.
DEMETRIUS An if I could, what should I get therefore?
HERMIA   A privilege never to see me more;
      And from thy hated presence part I so.   80
      See me no more, whether he be dead or no.

                                   [*Exit*

DEMETRIUS There is no following her in this fierce
        vein.
      Here therefore for a while I will remain.
      So sorrow's heaviness doth heavier grow
      For debt that bankrupt sleep doth sorrow owe;
      Which now in some slight measure it will pay,
      If for his tender here I make some stay.

He lies down and sleeps

OBERON What hast thou done? Thou hast mistaken
        quite,
      And laid the love-juice on some true-love's sight.
      Of thy misprision must perforce ensue   90
      Some true-love turned, and not a false turned
        true.
PUCK Then fate o'errules, that, one man holding
        troth,
      A million fail, confounding oath on oath.
OBERON About the wood go swifter than the wind,
      And Helena of Athens look thou find.
      All fancy-sick she is, and pale of cheer
      With sighs of love, that costs the fresh blood
        dear.
      By some illusion see thou bring her here.
      I'll charm his eyes against she do appear.

101   Tartar's bow *Bows of the Orient were thought to have magical powers.*

103   Hit . . . archery *See note to II. 1. 157–68.*
104   apple *pupil*

109   remedy *cure for love's wound – i.e. the acceptance of your suit*

113   lover's fee *repayment expected by the lover*
114   fond pageant *foolish exhibition*

119   alone *unique, pure*

121   befall *happen*
124   Look, when *It is possible that the comma may not be needed here, as 'Look when' could mean 'whenever'.*
        vows so . . . appears *vows thus originating in tears must certainly be true*
127   badge *The allusion is probably to the identifying insignia which retainers of noblemen wore on their sleeves. Lysander means his tears.*
128   advance *display*
129   When truth kills truth *When the truth you swear to me destroys the truth you formerly swore to Hermia*
        devilish-holy *'devilish' because truth is destroyed in the conflict between Lysander's vows; and 'holy' because the conflict is between oaths.*

102

PUCK   I go, I go – look how I go –   100
        Swifter than arrow from the Tartar's bow.

                                                        [*Exit*

OBERON   Flower of this purple dye,
                Hit with Cupid's archery,
                Sink in apple of his eye!

He squeezes the flower juice on DEMETRIUS'S *eyelids*
                When his love he doth espy,
                Let her shine as gloriously
                As the Venus of the sky.
                When thou wak'st, if she be by,
                Beg of her for remedy.

                Enter PUCK

PUCK   Captain of our fairy band,   110
                Helena is here at hand,
                And the youth, mistook by me,
                Pleading for a lover's fee.
                Shall we their fond pageant see?
                Lord, what fools these mortals be!

OBERON   Stand aside. The noise they make
                Will cause Demetrius to awake.

PUCK   Then will two at once woo one –
                That must needs be sport alone.
                And those things do best please me   120
                That do befall preposterously.

                Enter LYSANDER *and* HELENA

LYSANDER Why should you think that I should woo in
                scorn?
                Scorn and derision never come in tears.
                Look, when I vow, I weep; and vows so born,
                In their nativity all truth appears.
                How can these things in me seem scorn to you,
                Bearing the badge of faith to prove them true?

HELENA You do advance your cunning more and more.
                When truth kills truth, O devilish-holy fray!

                                                            103

130   give her o'er *renounce her*

131   Weigh oath with oath *Balance your oaths to Hermia*
                 against those you swear to me
               nothing weigh *be worthless because the scales will be*
                 equally balanced
133   as light as tales *as empty as fictions*

138   eyne *eyes*

141   Taurus *a range of mountains in Turkey*
142   Fanned with *Sifted by*

144   princess *paragon*
               seal *pledge*
145   spite *plague*
               bent *determined*
146   set against *attack*
147   civil *civilised*
148   injury *insult*

152   gentle *well-born or mild*
153   superpraise *praise extravagantly*
               parts *mental and physical qualities*

157   trim *fine (ironically)*

159   sort *quality, rank*
160   extort *torment*

These vows are Hermia's. Will you give her   130
  o'er?
Weigh oath with oath, and you will nothing
  weigh.
Your vows to her and me, put in two scales,
Will even weigh; and both as light as tales.

LYSANDER   I had no judgment when to her I swore.

HELENA   Nor none, in my mind, now you give her
  o'er.

LYSANDER   Demetrius loves her; and he loves not you.

DEMETRIUS [*Awaking*] O Helen, goddess, nymph,
  perfect, divine!
To what, my love, shall I compare thine eyne?
Crystal is muddy! O, how ripe in show
Thy lips – those kissing cherries – tempting
  grow!   140
That pure congealèd white, high Taurus' snow,
Fanned with the eastern wind, turns to a crow
When thou hold'st up thy hand. O, let me kiss
This princess of pure white, this seal of bliss.

HELENA   O spite! O hell! I see you all are bent
To set against me for your merriment.
If you were civil and knew courtesy,
You would not do me thus much injury.
Can you not hate me – as I know you do –
But you must join in souls to mock me too?   150
If you were men – as men you are in show –
You would not use a gentle lady so,
To vow, and swear, and superpraise my parts,
When I am sure you hate me with your hearts.
You both are rivals, and love Hermia;
And now both rivals to mock Helena.
A trim exploit, a manly enterprise –
To conjure tears up in a poor maid's eyes
With your derision! None of noble sort
Would so offend a virgin and extort   160
A poor soul's patience, all to make you sport.

168   idle *vain, useless*

169   I will none *I want no part of her*

171   My heart . . . sojourned *My heart, as it were, simply visited her*

175   aby it dear *dearly pay the penalty for it*

177   his *its*
        takes *takes away*

181   It pays . . . recompense *i.e. by making the hearing doubly acute*

183   thy sound *the sound of your voice*

189   oes and eyes *stars; 'oes' were sparkling orbs*

191   bare *felt towards*

LYSANDER You are unkind, Demetrius, Be not so!
    For you love Hermia – this you know I know.
    And here, with all good will, with all my heart,
    In Hermia's love I yield you up my part;
    And yours of Helena to me bequeath,
    Whom I do love, and will do till my death.

HELENA   Never did mockers waste more idle breath.

DEMETRIUS Lysander, keep thy Hermia! I will none.
    If e'er I loved her, all that love is gone.   170
    My heart to her but as guestwise sojourned,
    And now to Helen is it home returned.
    There to remain.

LYSANDER   Helen, it is not so.

DEMETRIUS Disparage not the faith thou dost not know
    Lest to thy peril thou aby it dear.
    Look where thy love comes. Yonder is thy dear.

Enter HERMIA

HERMIA Dark night, that from the eye his function
    takes,
    The ear more quick of apprehension makes.
    Wherein it doth impair the seeing sense,   180
    It pays the hearing double recompense.
    Thou art not by mine eye, Lysander, found;
    Mine ear – I thank it – brought me to thy sound
    But why unkindly didst thou leave me so?

LYSANDER Why should he stay whom love doth press
    to go?

HERMIA   What love could press Lysander from my
    side?

LYSANDER Lysander's love, that would not let him
    bide –
    Fair Helena, who more engilds the night
    Than all yon fiery oes and eyes of light.
    Why seek'st thou me? Could not this make thee
    know   190
    The hate I bare thee made me leave thee so?

195	in spite of *to vex, to spite*
196	Injurious *Insulting*
197	contrived *plotted*
198	bait *torment. Helena sees herself as a bear baited by dogs, which was a popular Elizabethan sport.*
199	counsel *secrets, confidences*
201	chid *reproached*
204	artificial *artistically skilful*
205	needle *Often pronounced and spelled 'neele'.*
206	sampler *work of embroidery*
207	both in one key *both in one mental and spiritual accord*
209	incorporate *of a single body*
211	partition *division*
215-16	Two of ... crest *Two bodies sharing a single heart. Helena's image is of an heraldic device which is formed by the joining of two coats of arms (as in the case of a man and a woman after their marriage), so that the new shield holds both and yet has a single 'crest' above them.*
214	the first *the first colours named in an official description of a coat of arms. This was a term in heraldry and serves to introduce the metaphor in lines 213-4.*
215	Due but to one *Belonging to only one person*
216	rent *tear, rend*
217	scorning *deriding*
221	amazèd *dumbfounded*
226	Who even ... foot *Compare II. 1. 205.* even but now *only a short while ago*

108

HERMIA   You speak not as you think. It cannot be.

HELENA   Lo, she is one of this confederacy.
          Now I perceive they have conjoined all three
          To fashion this false sport in spite of me.
          Injurious Hermia, most ungrateful maid,
          Have you conspired, have you with these
              contrived
          To bait me with this foul derision?
          Is all the counsel that we two have shared –
          The sister's vows, the hours that we have spent   200
          When we have chid the hasty-footed time
          For parting us – O, is all forgot?
          All schooldays' friendship, childhood
              innocence?
          We, Hermia, like two artificial gods,
          Have with our needles created both one flower,
          Both on one sampler, sitting on one cushion,
          Both warbling of one song, both in one key,
          As if our hands, our sides, voices, and minds
          Had been incorporate. So we grew together
          Like to a double cherry, seeming parted   210
          But yet an union in partition –
          Two lovely berries moulded on one stem;
          So, with two seeming bodies, but one heart,
          Two of the first, like coats in heraldry,
          Due but to one, and crownèd with one crest.
          And will you rent our ancient love asunder,
          To join with men in scorning your poor friend?
          It is not friendly, 'tis not maidenly.
          Our sex as well as I may chide you for it,
          Though I alone do feel the injury.   220

HERMIA   I am amazed at your passionate words.
          I scorn you not; it seems that you scorn me.

HELENA   Have you not set Lysander, as in scorn,
          To follow me and praise my eyes and face?
          And made your other love, Demetrius –
          Who even but now did spurn me with his foot –

230   your love *his love for you*
      rich *plentiful*
231   tender *offer*
232   by your consent *in accordance with your wishes*
233   so in grace *in so much favour*

238   Persever *Persevere. The accent is on the second syllable.*
      sad *grave, serious*
239   Make mouths *Pull faces*
240   hold . . . up *maintain the joke*
241   carried *carried out, executed*
      chronicled *recorded in history (a comic exaggeration)*
242   grace *good feeling*
243   argument *topic for fun, subject for mirth*

246   excuse *defence*

249   entreat *prevail by entreaty*

253   that which *i.e. his life*

256   withdraw *Let us go*
      prove it *i.e. by fighting a duel*

259   Ethiope *blackamoor (an insulting reference to Hermia's
      dark complexion)*

110

To call me goddess, nymph, divine and rare,
Precious, celestial? Wherefore speaks he this
To her he hates? And wherefore doth Lysander
Deny your love, so rich within his soul,   230
And tender me, forsooth, affection,
But by your setting on, by your consent?
What though I be not so in grace as you,
So hung upon with love, so fortunate,
But miserable most, to love unloved?
This you should pity rather than despise.

HERMIA I understand not what you mean by this.

HELENA Ay, do! Persever, counterfeit sad looks,
Make mouths upon me when I turn my back,
Wink at each other, hold the sweet jest up.   240
This sport, well carried, shall be chroniclèd.
If you have any pity, grace, or manners,
You would not make me such an argument.
But fare ye well. 'Tis partly my own fault,
Which death or absence soon shall remedy.

LYSANDER Stay, gentle Helena; hear my excuse,
My love, my life, my soul, fair Helena!

HELENA O excellent!

HERMIA [*To* LYSANDER] Sweet, do not scorn her so.

DEMETRIUS If she cannot entreat, I can compel.

LYSANDER Thou canst compel no more than she
entreat.   250
Thy threats have no more strength than her
weak prayers.
Helen, I love thee. By my life, I do!
I swear by that which I will lose for thee
To prove him false that says I love thee not.

DEMETRIUS I say I love thee more than he can do.

LYSANDER If thou say so, withdraw and prove it too.

DEMETRIUS Quick, come!

HERMIA [*Grasping* LYSANDER] Lysander, whereto tends
all this?

LYSANDER Away, you Ethiope!

260   Take on as *Pretend by exaggerated gestures*

261   go! *away with you!*

266   tawny Tartar *An insulting reference to Hermia's dark colouring*

267   med'cine . . . potion *Both these words could apply to any kind of drug including poison which is the meaning here.*

268   sooth *truly*

270   my word *my promise to fight*

271   bond *pledge*

272   bond *that which is binding you (i.e. Hermia)*

276   what news *what is the meaning of this*

278   erewhile *a short time ago*

279   Since *Since the commencement of*
         since *during the course of*

DEMETRIUS   No, no; he'll
    Seem to break loose. [*To* LYSANDER] Take on as
        you would follow,   260
    But yet come not? You are a tame man, go!
LYSANDER   Hang off, thou cat, thou burr! Vile thing,
        let loose,
    Or I will shake thee from me like a serpent.
HERMIA   Why are you grown so rude? What change is
        this,
    Sweet love?
LYSANDER   Thy love? Out, tawny Tartar, out!
    Out loathèd med'cine! O hated potion, hence!
HERMIA   Do you not jest?
HELENA   Yes, sooth; and so do you.
LYSANDER   Demetrius, I will keep my word with thee. 270
DEMETRIUS   I would I had your bond, for I perceive
    A weak bond holds you. I'll not trust your
        word.
LYSANDER   What, should I hurt her, strike her, kill her
        dead?
    Although I hate her, I'll not harm her so.
HERMIA   What? Can you do me greater harm than
        hate?
    Hate me? Wherefore? O me, what news, my
        love?
    Am not I Hermia? Are not you Lysander?
    I am as fair now as I was erewhile.
    Since night you loved me; yet since night you
        left me.
    Why then, you left me – O, the gods forbid! –
    In earnest, shall I say?   280
LYSANDER   Ay, by my life;
    And never did desire to see thee more.
    Therefore be out of hope, of question, of
        doubt –
    Be certain. Nothing truer. 'Tis no jest
    That I do hate thee, and love Helena.

285   juggler *trickster*
canker blossom *The term meant 'wild rose'; but here
the meaning seems to be the canker worm that eats at
the flower.*

287   Fine i' faith *Helena is still convinced that Hermia is
in league with the two men, and expresses mock
admiration at what she takes to be a pretended display of fury by Hermia.*

291   counterfeit *imitation of a woman (because in Helena's
view Hermia has forsaken womenly feelings and
loyalties)*
puppet *The reference is to Hermia's small stature.*

293   compare *comparison*
294   urged *produced as a quality in her favour*

297   so high in his esteem *so well regarded by him; with
pun on 'high' meaning 'tall'.*

299   painted maypole *The reference is again to Helena's
height, but Hermia further suggests that her pink and
white complexion is the result of cosmetics.*

303   curst *shrewish, quarrelsome*

305   right maid *i.e. quite unmanly*

308   can match her *am a match for her in a fight*

312   counsels *secrets*

314   stealth *secret flight*

HERMIA O me! [*To* HELENA] You juggler, you canker blossom,
You thief of love! What, have you come by night
And stol'n my love's heart from him?

HELENA   Fine, i' faith.
Have you no modesty, no maiden shame,
No touch of bashfulness? What, will you tear
Impatient answers from my gentle tongue?   290
Fie, fie, you counterfeit, you puppet you!

HERMIA Puppet! Why so? – Ay, that way goes the game.
Now I perceive that she hath made compare
Between our statures. She hath urged her height,
And with her personage, her tall personage,
Her height, forsooth, she hath prevailed with him.
And are you grown so high in his esteem
Because I am so dwarfish and so low?
How low am I, thou painted maypole? Speak!
How low am I? I am not yet so low   300
But that my nails can reach unto thine eyes.

HELENA I pray you, though you mock me, gentlemen,
Let her not hurt me. I was never curst;
I have no gift at all in shrewishness;
I am a right maid for my cowardice.
Let her not strike me. You perhaps may think
Because she is something lower than myself
That I can match her.

HERMIA   'Lower'? Hark again!

HELENA Good Hermia, do not be so bitter with me.   310
I evermore did love you, Hermia,
Did ever keep your counsels, never wronged you;
Save that in love unto Demetrius,
I told him of your stealth unto this wood.
He followed you; for love I followed him.

318   so *provided that*
        quiet *peacefully*

321   fond *foolish*

328   keen *sharp-tongued*
        shrewd *shrewish, vixenish*

332   flout *mock, jeer at*

335   minimus *smallest creature*
        knotgrass *a ground weed the juice of which was popularly thought to stunt growth*

339   intend *pretend, give sign of*

341   aby *pay for*
        she *i.e. Hermia*

343   try *test, make trial of*

But he hath chid me hence, and threatened me
To strike me, spurn me – nay, to kill me too.
And now, so you will let me quiet go,
To Athens will I bear my folly back
And follow you no further. Let me go.   320
You see how simple and how fond I am.

HERMIA   Why, get you gone! Who is't that hinders
          you?
HELENA   A foolish heart that I leave here behind.
HERMIA   What, with Lysander?
HELENA   With Demetrius.
LYSANDER Be not afraid; she shall not harm thee,
          Helena.
DEMETRIUS No, sir. She shall not, though you take her
          part.
HELENA   O, when she's angry, she is keen and
          shrewd.
          She was a vixen when she went to school;
          And though she be but little, she is fierce.   330
HERMIA   'Little' again? Nothing but 'low' and 'little'?
          Why will you suffer her to flout me thus?
          Let me come to her.
LYSANDER   Get you gone, you dwarf!
          You minimus of hindering knotgrass made,
          You bead, you acorn!
DEMETRIUS   You are too officious
          In her behalf that scorns your services.
          Let her alone. Speak not of Helena;
          Take not her part. For if thou dost intend
          Never so little show of love to her,   340
          Thou shalt aby it.
LYSANDER   Now she holds me not.
          Now follow – if thou dar'st – to try whose right,
          Of thine or mine, is most in Helena.
DEMETRIUS Follow? Nay, I'll go with thee, cheek by
          jowl.

                    [*Exeunt* LYSANDER *and* DEMETRIUS

346   coil *trouble, turmoil*
'long of *on account of*

348   curst *shrewish*

351   amazed *in utter bewilderment*

352   Still *Always, ever*

359   so far *at least to this extent*
sort *happen, turn out*

360   As *In that*
jangling *noisy quarrelling*

362   Hie *Hurry, go*
363   welkin *sky*
364   Acheron *one of the black rivers of the Classical underworld*
365   testy *choleric*
366   As *So that*
367   frame thy tongue *make your voice sound*
368   wrong *insult*

371   death-counterfeiting *sleep as the image of death was a common idea and is used elsewhere by Shakespeare*
372   batty *bat-like*
374   liquor *juice*
virtuous *potent, powerful*
375   his might *its strength*
376   wonted *usual, accustomed*
377   derision *laughable delusion*
378   fruitless *useless, meaningless*

118

HERMIA You, mistress – all this coil is 'long of you.
    Nay, go not back.
HELENA   I will not trust you, I,
    Nor longer stay in your curst company.
    Your hands than mine are quicker for a fray;
    My legs are longer, though, to run away.   350
                     [*Exit*

HERMIA I am amazed, and know not what to say.
                     [*Exit*

    OBERON *and* PUCK *come forward*
OBERON This is thy negligence. Still thou mistak'st,
    Or else commit'st thy knaveries wilfully.
PUCK   Believe me, King of Shadows, I mistook.
    Did not you tell me I should know the man
    By the Athenian garments he had on?
    And so far blameless proves my enterprise
    That I have 'nointed an Athenian's eyes;
    And so far am I glad it so did sort
    As this their jangling I esteem a sport.   360
OBERON Thou seest these lovers seek a place to fight.
    Hie therefore, Robin, overcast the night.
    The starry welkin cover thou anon
    With drooping fog as black as Acheron,
    And lead these testy rivals so astray
    As one come not within another's way.
    Like to Lysander sometime frame thy tongue,
    Then stir Demetrius up with bitter wrong,
    And sometime rail thou like Demetrius;
    And from each other look thou lead them thus 370
    Till o'er their brows death-counterfeiting sleep
    With leaden legs and batty wings doth creep.
    Then crush this herb into Lysander's eye,
    Whose liquor hath this virtuous property,
    To take from thence all error with his might
    And make his eyeballs roll with wonted sight.
    When they next wake, all this derision
    Shall seem a dream and fruitless vision,

379   wend *make their way*
380   league *union*
        date *duration, term*
381   Whiles *Whilst*

383   charmèd *affected by a charm, bewitched*

386   night's swift dragons *The allusion may be to Medea's
        team of dragons given her by Hecate, which Ovid
        records in his* Metamorphoses.
387   Aurora's harbinger *the morning star which heralds the
        approach of the goddess Aurora (the dawn)*

389   Damnèd spirits *the ghosts of damned souls*

390   in crossways and floods *Suicides were buried at cross
        roads. 'Floods' probably refers to victims of either
        suicidal or accidental drowning whose spirits were
        reputed to wander in the night because burial rites
        had not been accorded their corpses.*
391   wormy beds *graves*
392   shames *This noun often had a plural form in Eliza-
        bethan English when more than one person was
        concerned.*
394   aye *ever*
395–400 But we ... streams *Shakespeare is making clear here
        that Oberon, unlike other fairies and spirits is not
        forced to flee the day. Compare note to II. 1. 267.*
396   I with ... sport *There are two possible meanings: (1)
        that Oberon has often chased game with the famous
        hunter Cephalus, who was loved by Aurora; (2) that
        Oberon has made love with the goddess Aurora her-
        self.*
399   Neptune *the ocean*
401   haste *make haste*

406   Goblin *Puck is here addressing himself.*

And back to Athens shall the lovers wend
With league whose date till death shall never
 end.   380
Whiles I in this affair do thee employ,
I'll to my Queen and beg her Indian boy;
And then I will her charmèd eye release
From monster's view, and all things shall be
 peace.

PUCK My fairy lord, this must be done with haste,
  For night's swift dragons cut the clouds full
   fast,
  And yonder shines Aurora's harbinger,
  At whose approach ghosts wand'ring here and
   there
  Troop home to churchyards. Damnèd spirits
   all
  That in crossways and floods have burial   390
  Already to their wormy beds are gone.
  For fear lest day should look their shames
   upon,
  They wilfully themselves exile from light,
  And must for aye consort with black-browed
   night.

OBERON But we are spirits of another sort.
  I with the morning's love have oft made sport,
  And like a forester the groves may tread
  Even till the eastern gate, all fiery red,
  Opening on Neptune, with fair blessèd beams
  Turns into yellow gold his salt green streams.   400
  But notwithstanding, haste: make no delay.
  We may effect this business yet ere day.

             [*Exit*

PUCK   Up and down, up and down,
    I will lead them up and down.
    I am feared in field and town.
    Goblin, lead them up and down.
  Here comes one.

407–440   *It is usual in editions of the play to clarify the action here by indicating that Lysander and Demetrius go on and off the stage led by Puck. However, in performance the action can be comically managed by having the two young men grope about in the darkness while Puck darts from one to the other.*

409   drawn *with my sword drawn*

410   straight *immediately*

411   plainer *open and more level*

417   recreant *coward*

418   defiled *disgraced, dishonoured*

421–2   try no manhood *have no test of manly courage*

423   still dares me on *always challenges me to follow*

427   That *With the result that*

in *into*

Enter LYSANDER

LYSANDER Where art thou, proud Demetrius? Speak
    thou now.

PUCK [*In* DEMETRIUS'S *voice*] Here, villain, drawn and
    ready. Where art thou?

LYSANDER I will be with thee straight.   410

PUCK [*In* DEMETRIUS'S *voice*]   Follow me then
      To plainer ground.   [*Exit* LYSANDER

Enter DEMETRIUS

DEMETRIUS   Lysander, speak again!
    Thou runaway, thou coward, art thou fled?
    Speak! In some bush? Where dost thou hide thy
      head?

PUCK [*In* LYSANDER'S *voice*] Thou coward, art thou
    bragging to the stars,
    Telling the bushes that thou look'st for wars,
    And wilt not come? Come, recreant! Come,
      thou child!
    I'll whip thee with a rod. He is defiled
    That draws a sword on thee.

DEMETRIUS   Yea, art thou there?   420

PUCK [*In* LYSANDER'S *voice*] Follow my voice, We'll try
    no manhood here.

                        [*Exeunt*

Enter LYSANDER

LYSANDER He goes before me and still dares me on;
    When I come where he calls, then he is gone.
    The villain is much lighter-heeled than I.
    I followed fast, but faster he did fly,
    That fallen am I in dark uneven way,
    And here will rest me. [*He lies down*] Come,
      thou gentle day,
    For if but once thou show me thy grey light,
    I'll find Demetrius and revenge this spite.

                        [*He sleeps*

430   Ho, ho, ho! *This was Puck's traditional cry and is used in other plays of the period to signalise his entrance.*

431   Abide *Wait for*
        wot *know*

432   shifting *moving from*

436   buy this dear *pay dearly for this*

440   visited *sought out and attacked*

442   Abate *Make shorter*
        Shine . . . East *May the sustaining daylight shine*

444   my poor company *the company of my unfortunate self*

449   curst *cross, out of humour*

454   go *walk*

124

Enter PUCK *and* DEMETRIUS

PUCK [*In* LYSANDER'S *voice*] Ho, ho, ho! Coward, why
      com'st thou not?   430

DEMETRIUS Abide me if thou dar'st, for well I wot
      Thou runn'st before me, shifting every place,
      And dar'st not stand nor look me in the face.
      Where art thou now?

PUCK [*In* LYSANDER'S *voice*] Come hither; I am here.

DEMETRIUS Nay then, thou mock'st me. Thou shalt
      buy this dear
      If ever I thy face by daylight see.
      Now go thy way. Faintness constraineth me
      To measure out my length on this cold bed.
      By day's approach look to be visited.   440
                          [*He lies down and sleeps*

Enter HELENA

HELENA O weary night! O long and tedious night,
      Abate thy hours. Shine comforts from the East,
      That I may back to Athens by daylight
      From these that my poor company detest;
      And sleep, that sometimes shuts up sorrow's
      eye,
      Steal me awhile from mine own company.
                     [*She lies down and sleeps*

PUCK   Yet but three? Come one more.
      Two of both kinds makes up four.
      Here she comes, curst and sad.
      Cupid is a knavish lad   450
      Thus to make poor females mad.

Enter HERMIA

HERMIA Never so weary, never so in woe,
      Bedabbled with the dew, and torn with briers –
      I can no further crawl, no further go;
      My legs can keep no pace with my desires.

457   mean a fray *intend to fight*

471   Jack . . . Jill *Every man shall have his own woman (a proverb)*

473   The man . . . again *All will turn out well (a proverb)*

Here will I rest me till the break of day.
Heavens shield Lysander, if they mean a fray!

[*She lies down and sleeps*

PUCK   On the ground
                    Sleep sound.
                    I'll apply   460
                    To your eye,
                    Gentle lover, remedy.

He squeezes the herb juice on LYSANDER'S *eyelids*

                    When thou wak'st,
                    Thou tak'st
                    True delight
                    In the sight
Of thy former lady's eye;
And the country proverb known,
That every man should take his own,
In your waking shall be shown.   470
                    Jack shall have Jill,
                    Naught shall go ill,
The man shall have his mare again, and all
    shall be well.

[*Exit*

ACT FOUR, scene 1

Oberon witnesses the full working out of his punishment of Titania, and is reconciled to her. The Lovers and Bottom are awakened and all try to recapture in rational terms the quality of their dream experience. There is no real break between this scene and the previous one. The four lovers sleep on the stage during the scene between Bottom and Titania, unnoticed by them. One of the early texts of the play notes at the end of III. 2 in a stage direction 'they sleep all the Act' which may indicate that this is what happened in Shakespeare's theatre.

2	amiable *lovely*
	coy *caress, stroke*
3	musk-roses *dog-roses*
8	Mounsieur *Bottom's mispronunciation of 'Monsieur' is indicated in the earliest printed text of the play.*
10	humble-bee *bumble-bee*
12	fret *trouble*
14	would be loath *would not like*
	overflown *covered, deluged*
18	neaf *hand, fist*
19	leave your curtsy *do not bow and scrape to me; do not stand on ceremony*
22	Cavalery Cobweb *The title is Bottom's attempt at pronouncing either the Italian* cavaliere *or the Spanish* caballero. *The fairy addressed is Pease-blossom, as Cobweb has been sent on an errand by Bottom at ll. 10–16 the error may be Bottom's or may simply be an oversight on Shakespeare's part.*
23	marvellous *exceptionally*

ACT FOUR

Scene 1. *Enter* TITANIA, *Queen of Fairies, and* BOTTOM, *the Clown, and Fairies,* PEASEBLOSSOM, COBWEB, MOTH, MUSTARDSEED *and others; and the King of Fairies,* OBERON, *behind them.*

TITANIA   Come, sit thee down upon this flowery bed,
      While I thy amiable cheeks do coy
      And stick musk-roses in thy sleek smooth head
      And kiss thy fair large ears, my gentle joy.
BOTTOM   Where's Peaseblossom?
PEASEBLOSSOM   Ready.
BOTTOM   Scratch my head, Peaseblossom. Where's Mounsieur Cobweb?
COBWEB   Ready.
BOTTOM   Mounsieur Cobweb, good Mounsieur, get you your weapons in your hand, and kill me a red-hipped humble-bee on the top of a thistle; and, good mounsieur, bring me the honey-bag. Do not fret yourself too much in the action, Mounsieur; and, good Mounsieur, have a care the honey-bag break not. I would be loath to have you overflown with a honey-bag, Signior. Where's Mounsieur Mustardseed?
MUSTARDSEED   Ready.
BOTTOM   Give me your neaf, Mounsieur Mustardseed. Pray you, leave your curtsy, good Mounsieur.
MUSTARDSEED   What's your will?
BOTTOM   Nothing, good Mounsieur, but to help Cavalery Cobweb to scratch. I must to the barber's, Mounsieur; for methinks I am marvellous hairy about the face – and I am such a tender ass, if my hair do but tickle me, I must scratch.
TITANIA   What, wilt thou hear some music, my sweet love?

28   tongs and the bones *Both crude musical instruments, the tongs were struck with a piece of metal, and the bones were flat bone clappers held between the fingers of one hand and rattled against each other by shaking the hand. One of the early texts of the play has the stage direction calling for 'rural music' at this point. Such a sound effect would underline the plight of Titania who is usually associated with a quite different kind of music.*

30   peck *a quarter of a bushel*

32   bottle *small bundle*
      hath no fellow *has no equal*

36   pease *This was both the singular and the plural form of the word during the Elizabethan period.*
      stir *disturb*

37   exposition *Bottom means 'disposition' i.e. inclination*

38   wind *wrap*

39   all ways *in all directions*

40   woodbine *Woodbine is honeysuckle and is used as such at II. 1. 252. It is possible that the second meaning 'bindweed, convolvulus' is intended here.*

41   female *i.e. because it clings to and is supported by the elm*

45   dotage *doting*

47   favours *floral love tokens*

51   sometime *formerly, once*

52   orient *lustrous*

54   disgrace *i.e. because they adorn Bottom's ass-head*

BOTTOM I have a reasonable good ear in music. Let's
have the tongs and the bones.

TITANIA Or say, sweet love, what thou desirest to eat.

BOTTOM Truly, a peck of provender. I could munch   30
your good dry oats. Methinks I have a great desire
to a bottle of hay. Good hay, sweet hay, hath no
fellow.

TITANIA I have a venturous fairy that shall seek
The squirrel's hoard, and fetch thee new nuts.

BOTTOM I had rather have a handful or two of dried
pease. But, I pray you, let none of your people stir
me. I have an exposition of sleep come upon me.

TITANIA Sleep thou, and I will wind thee in my arms.
Fairies, be gone, and be all ways away.

> [*Exeunt* FAIRIES

So doth the woodbine the sweet honeysuckle   40
Gently entwist; the female ivy so
Enrings the barky fingers of the elm.
O, how I love thee! How I dote on thee!

> [BOTTOM *and* TITANIA *sleep*

Enter PUCK

OBERON [*Coming forward*] Welcome, good Robin,
Seest thou this sweet sight?
Her dotage now I do begin to pity;
For, meeting her of late behind the wood,
Seeking sweet favours for this hateful fool,
I did upbraid her and fall out with her.
For she his hairy temples then had rounded
With coronet of fresh and fragrant flowers.   50
And that same dew which sometime on the buds
Was wont to swell like round and orient pearls,
Stood now within the pretty flowerets' eyes
Like tears that did their own disgrace bewail.
When I had at my pleasure taunted her,
And she in mild terms begged my patience,
I then did ask of her her changeling child,

58   straight *immediately*

64   other *others*
65   May *They may*
              repair *go*
66   accidents *happenings, incidents*
67   fierce *extravagant*

71   Dian's bud *the herb mentioned at II. 1. 184 and III. 2.
             373. Diana was reputed to carry a flower which
             preserved chastity called* agnus castus.
             Cupid's flower *the flower mentioned at II. 1. 166–72.*

76   to pass *to happen*

78   Silence awhile! *Presumably the command is to Titania
             so that the sleeping lovers of whom she is at the
             moment unaware will not awaken before Oberon can
             put his charm upon them.*
79–80   Titania ... sense *Titania call for some music and
             plunge the senses of these five (the four lovers and
             Bottom) into the deepest of sleeps*
81   charmeth sleep *produces sleep as by a magic spell*

84   rock the ground *Oberon sees the fairy dance as pro-
             ducing a cradle-like movement of the ground.*

85   new in amity *in renewed concord*
86   solemnly *with ceremony*

132

Which straight she gave me, and her fairy sent
To bear him to my bower in Fairyland.
And now I have the boy, I will undo   60
This hateful imperfection of her eyes.
And, gentle Puck, take this transformèd scalp
From off the head of this Athenian swain;
That, he awaking when the other do,
May all to Athens back again repair,
And think no more of this night's accidents
But as the fierce vexation of a dream.
But first I will release the Fairy Queen.
[*To* TITANIA]
    Be as thou wast wont to be;
    See as thou wast wont to see.   70
    Dian's bud o'er Cupid's flower
    Hath such force and blessèd power.
He squeezes the herb juice on TITANIA'S *eyelids*
    Now, my Titania, wake you, my sweet Queen.
TITANIA [*Awaking*] My Oberon, what visions have I
    seen!
    Methought I was enamoured of an ass.
OBERON There lies your love.
TITANIA   How came these things to pass?
    O, how mine eyes do loathe his visage now!
OBERON Silence awhile! Robin, take off this head.
    Titania, music call, and strike more dead
    Than common sleep of all these five the sense.   80
TITANIA Music, ho! Music such as charmeth sleep.
PUCK [*To* BOTTOM *while removing the ass's head*] Now,
    when thou wak'st, with thine own fool's eyes
    peep.
OBERON Sound, music! [*Music*] Come, my Queen,
    take hands with me,
    And rock the ground whereon these sleepers be.
                        [*They dance*
    Now thou and I are new in amity,
    And will to-morrow midnight solemnly

88   prosperity *Some early texts of the play have 'posterity' here which is a possible reading.*

93   sad *sober, serious*

95   We the globe . . . soon *Compare Puck's claim at II. 1 175–6.*

98   came *came about*

100   Wind horn *A common stage direction of the time. Horns were used as signalling instruments in Elizabethan theatres. Here, however, they are appropriate in that Theseus is hunting.*

101   forester *controller of the game and cover in a royal forest*

102   observation *observance of the rites of Mayday morning see note to I. 1. 167.*

103   vaward *forepart, earliest part. The word means literally 'vanguard'.*

105   Uncouple *Release the hounds (which have been leashed together in pairs)*

107   will *will go*

110–12   I was . . . Sparta *There is no authority in Greek mythology for this. In some stories Theseus was the companion of Hercules in his Amazonian exploits. Sparta and Crete were both famous for their hunting dogs in Classical times.*

111   bayed the bear *brought the bear to bay (i.e. to make its final stand)*

113   chiding *barking*

118   flewed *possessing flews (i.e. pendulous chaps)*
         sanded *sand-coloured*

134

Dance in Duke Theseus' house triumphantly
And bless it to all fair prosperity.
There shall the pairs of faithful lovers be
Wedded, with Theseus, all in jollity.   90

PUCK   Fairy King, attend and mark:
            I do hear the morning lark.

OBERON   Then, my Queen, in silence sad
            Trip we after night's shade.
            We the globe can compass soon,
            Swifter than the wandering moon.

TITANIA   Come, my lord, and in our flight
            Tell me how it came this night
            That I sleeping here was found
            With these mortals on the ground.   100

            [*Exeunt* OBERON, TITANIA, *and* PUCK

Wind horn. Enter THESEUS *with* HIPPOLYTA *and*
            EGEUS *and all his Train*

THESEUS Go, one of you; find out the forester,
            For now our observation is performed;
            And since we have the vaward of the day,
            My love shall hear the music of my hounds.
            Uncouple in the western valley; let them go.
            Dispatch, I say, and find the forester.

                                    [*Exit a* SERVANT

            We will, fair Queen, up to the mountain's top
            And mark the musical confusion
            Of hounds and echo in conjunction.

HIPPOLYTA I was with Hercules and Cadmus once   110
            When in a wood of Crete they bayed the bear
            With hounds of Sparta. Never did I hear
            Such gallant chiding; for, besides the groves,
            The skies, the fountains, every region near
            Seemed all one mutual cry. I never heard
            So musical a discord, such sweet thunder.

THESEUS My hounds are bred out of the Spartan kind:
            So flewed, so sanded; and their heads are hung

120   dewlapped *with hanging chaps*
       Thessalian *of Thessaly, a northern part of ancient
           Greece*
121–2 but matched . . . each *The ideal cry of a hunting pack
           was considered to consist of a number of large dogs
           with deep baying voices, double this number of dogs
           with lighter barks, and a few dogs which could bark
           in the intermediate range.*
122   cry *pack of hounds*
       tuneable *melodious*
125   soft! *stand!, wait a moment!*
       nymphs *i.e. wood dwellers*

129   I wonder of *I am surprised at*
130   to observe *to do observance to*

132   in grace of *in honour of*
       solemnity *festivity, festival*
134   her choice *See I. 1. 83–90.*

137   Saint Valentine . . . now *Saint Valentine's Day 14
           February was traditionally the birds wedding day.*

140   rival enemies *enemies owing to your rivalry (for
           Hermia)*
142   jealousy *suspicion*
143   by hate *by the side of one who hates you*
144   amazedly *confusedly*

With ears that sweep away the morning dew;
Crook-kneed, and dewlapped like Thessalian
    bulls;   120
Slow in pursuit, but matched in mouth like
    bells,
Each under each. A cry more tuneable
Was never hallooed to nor cheered with horn
In Crete, in Sparta, nor in Thessaly.
Judge when you hear. [*He sees the four lovers*]
    But soft! What nymphs are these?

EGEUS My lord, this is my daughter here asleep;
And this, Lysander; this Demetrius is;
This Helena, old Nedar's Helena.
I wonder of their being here together.

THESEUS No doubt they rose up early to observe   130
The rite of May; and, hearing our intent,
Came here in grace of our solemnity.
But speak, Egeus: is not this the day
That Hermia should give answer of her choice?

EGEUS   It is, my lord.

THESEUS Go, bid the huntsmen wake them with their
    horns.
    [*Exit a* SERVANT. *Wind horns. The lovers awake
    and start up*

Good morrow, friends. Saint Valentine is past!
Begin these woodbirds but to couple now?

LYSANDER Pardon, my lord.
                      [*The lovers kneel*

THESEUS   I pray you all, stand up.
I know you two are rival enemies.   140
How comes this gentle concord in the world,
That hatred is so far from jealousy
To sleep by hate and fear no enmity?

LYSANDER My lord, I shall reply amazedly,
Half sleep, half waking; but as yet, I swear
I cannot truly say how I came here.
But, as I think – for truly would I speak –

150   where we might *wherever we could*
151   Without *Outside, beyond*
152   Enough *Enough evidence of his guilt*

155   defeated *deprived*

158   stealth *stealing away*
159   purpose hither *purpose in coming hither*

161   in fancy *driven by love*
162   wot *know*

165   idle gaud *valueless toy*

167   virtue *power*

171   like a sickness *like one with a sickness*
172   come *having returned*

177   overbear *overrule*

179   knit *joined*
180   something worn *somewhat spent*

And now I do bethink me, so it is:
I came with Hermia hither. Our intent
Was to be gone from Athens, where we might 150
Without the peril of the Athenian law –

EGEUS Enough, enough, my lord! You have enough!
I beg the law, the law upon his head.
They would have stol'n away; they would,
    Demetrius,
Thereby to have defeated you and me –
You of your wife, and me of my consent,
Of my consent that she should be your wife.

DEMETRIUS My lord, fair Helen told me of their
    stealth,
Of this their purpose hither to this wood,
And I in fury hither followed them,   160
Fair Helena in fancy following me.
But, my good lord – I wot not by what power,
But by some power it is – my love to Hermia,
Melted as the snow, seems to me now
As the remembrance of an idle gaud
Which in my childhood I did dote upon;
And all the faith, the virtue of my heart,
The object and the pleasure of mine eye,
Is only Helena. To her, my lord,
Was I betrothed ere I saw Hermia,   170
But, like a sickness, did I loathe this food;
But, as in health, come to my natural taste,
Now I do wish it, love it, long for it,
And will for evermore be true to it.

THESEUS Fair lovers, you are fortunately met.
Of this discourse we more will hear anon.
Egeus, I will overbear your will;
For in the temple by and by with us
These couples shall eternally be knit.
And – for the morning now is something worn– 180
Our purposed hunting shall be set aside.
Away with us to Athens! Three and three,

183   solemnity *festivity, splendour*

185   These things *i.e. surroundings*

187   parted eye *divided vision*

189–90   like a jewel . . . own *like something precious which I have found but which I fear may yet not belong to me*

198–9   Hey-ho! *A yawn; but the actor in modern productions often says this with a trace of 'hee-haw'.*

200   God's my life! *A common oath; possibly a contraction of 'God save my life!'*

201   vision *The same word is noticeably used by Oberon at III. 2. 378, Titania at IV. 1. 74, and Puck at V. 1. 417. For comment on this see the Introduction pp. 18–20.*

202   wit *intellect, mental powers*

203   go about *try, undertake*

206   patched fool *a jester who wears a parti-coloured costume*

207–10   The eye . . . dream was *This is Bottom's confused recollection of I Corinthians 2.9 'The eye hath not seen, and the ear hath not heard, neither have entered into the heart of man, the things which God hath prepared for them that love him.'*

We'll hold a feast in great solemnity.
Come, Hippolyta.

[*Exeunt* THESEUS, HIPPOLYTA, EGEUS, *and* ATTENDANTS

DEMETRIUS These things seem small and
           undistinguishable,
    Like far-off mountains turnèd into clouds.

HERMIA Methinks I see these things with parted eye,
    When everything seems double.

HELENA   So methinks;
    And I have found Demetrius, like a jewel,
    Mine own and not mine own.

DEMETRIUS   Are you sure   190
    That we are awake? It seems to me
    That yet we sleep, we dream. Do not you think
    The Duke was here, and bid us follow him?

HERMIA   Yea, and my father.

HELENA   And Hippolyta.

LYSANDER And he did bid us follow to the temple.

DEMETRIUS Why then, we are awake. Let's follow him,
    And by the way let us recount our dreams.

[*Exeunt* LYSANDER, HERMIA, DEMETRIUS, *and* HELENA

BOTTOM [*Awaking*] When my cue comes, call me, and
I will answer. My next is 'Most fair Pyramus.' Hey-
ho! Peter Quince? Flute the bellows-mender? Snout
the tinker? Starveling? God's my life! Stolen hence 200
and left me asleep! I have had a most rare vision. I
have had a dream, past the wit of man to say what
dream it was. Man is but an ass if he go about to
expound this dream. Methought I was – there is no
man can tell what. Methought I was – and methought I had – but man is but a patched fool if he
will offer to say what methought I had. The eye of
man hath not heard, the ear of man hath not seen,
man's hand is not able to taste, his tongue to conceive, nor his heart to report what my dream was. 210
I will get Peter Quince to write a ballad of this
dream. It shall be called 'Bottom's Dream', because

213   hath no bottom *is unfathomable, has no foundation in reality*

214   Peradventure *Perhaps, not improbably*

215   gracious *pleasing*

         her death *Presumably at the death of Thisbe. Note Bottom's desire at V. 1. 345–7 to prolong the entertainment in some way.*

ACT FOUR, scene 2

The scene is located in Athens and serves to reintroduce us to the Mechanicals who left the play in III. 1, and prepares for their participation in the wedding celebration in V. 1.

3   Out of doubt *Certainly*

4   transported *carried off (by spirits)*

8   discharge *perform the rôle of*

9   wit *intellect, brain*

9–10   handicraft man *tradesman*

11   person *figure, appearance*

12   paramour *illegal lover*

14   thing of naught *a wicked thing (literally 'a thing of no value')*

17   gone forward *taken place*

18   made men *men whose fortunes would have been made*

19   bully *good fellow*

19–21   sixpence a day *i.e. a pension of this amount given by Theseus. In sixteenth-century England sixpence was quite a substantial sum.*

         An *If*

25   hearts *fine fellows*

27   courageous *encouraging, auspicious (?)*

         happy *lucky, fortunate*

it hath no bottom; and I will sing it in the latter end
of our play before the Duke. Peradventure, to make
it the more gracious, I shall sing it at her death.

[*Exit*

Scene 2. *Enter* QUINCE, FLUTE, SNOUT, *and* STARVELING

QUINCE Have you sent to Bottom's house? Is he come
home yet?

STARVELING He cannot be heard of. Out of doubt he is
transported.

FLUTE If he come not, then the play is marred. It goes
not forward, doth it?

QUINCE It is not possible. You have not a man in all
Athens able to discharge Pyramus but he.

FLUTE No, he hath simply the best wit of any handicraft man in Athens. 10

QUINCE Yea, and the best person, too; and he is a very
paramour for a sweet voice.

FLUTE You must say 'paragon'. A paramour is – God
bless us – a thing of naught.

Enter SNUG *the joiner*

SNUG Masters, the Duke is coming from the temple,
and there is two or three lords and ladies more
married. If our sport had gone forward, we had all
been made men.

FLUTE O, sweet bully Bottom! Thus hath he lost sixpence a day during his life. He could not have 20
scaped sixpence a day. An the Duke had not given
him sixpence a day for playing Pyramus, I'll be
hanged. He would have deserved it. Sixpence a day
in Pyramus, or nothing.

Enter BOTTOM

BOTTOM Where are these lads? Where are these hearts?

QUINCE Bottom! O most courageous day! O most
happy hour!

28   I am *I have to*

30   right *exactly*
           fell out *happened*

32   of me *from me, out of me*

35   presently *immediately*

37   preferred *recommended, placed on the list for favour-*
           able consideration
      In any case *But however it turns out so far as the*
           selection of our entertainment is concerned

38   pare *clip, cut*

41   breath *(1) exhalation, and (2) words*

BOTTOM Masters, I am to discourse wonders – but ask
me not what; for if I tell you, I am no true Athenian
– I will tell you everything, right as it fell out. 30

QUINCE Let us hear, sweet Bottom.

BOTTOM Not a word of me! All that I will tell you is,
that the Duke hath dined. Get your apparel together,
good strings to your beards, new ribbons to your
pumps. Meet presently at the palace. Every man
look o'er his part; for the short and the long is, our
play is preferred. In any case, let Thisbe have clean
linen; and let not him that plays the lion pare his
nails, for they shall hang out for the lion's claws.
And, most dear actors, eat no onions nor garlic; for 40
we are to utter sweet breath, and I do not doubt but
to hear them say it is a sweet comedy. No more
words. Away! Go, away!

[*Exeunt*

ACT FIVE, scene 1

This scene draws together all of the threads of the plots and the themes which have been explored. In contrast to the Athens of the opening scene, here there is concord, marriage, celebration, and entertainment. The Pyramus and Thisbe playlet reminds us of the tragic possibilities avoided in the play itself. As the scene ends Theseus's palace is invaded by the spirits of the wood and the night, now no longer forces of disruption but the promises of a happy future for the newly married couples.

1–22	'Tis strange . . . bear? *For discussion of these lines see the Introduction, p. 17.*
3	antique *both 'grotesque' and 'ancient'*
	fairy toys *idle or silly tales about fairies*
4	seething *boiling*
5	fantasies *imaginations*
	apprehend *imagine, conceive*
6	comprehends *understands*
8	compact *composed*
10	frantic *wild*
11	Helen *i.e. Helen of Troy, the most beautiful woman of the ancient world*
	brow of Egypt *the face of a gypsy. The Elizabethans' ideal of feminine beauty was fair hair and a pale complexion.*
14	bodies forth *gives physical shape to*
19–20	That if . . . joy *i.e. that if the imagination wishes to conceive the joy then it includes, as part of what it apprehends, some non-existent person who brings the joy. Theseus' point is that the human imagination has a strong tendency towards personification when envisaging abstractions.*
20	comprehends *includes*
24	transfigured so together *changed at the same time*
25	More . . . images *testifies to something more than fanciful notions produced by the imagination*
26	grows to *amounts to*
	constancy *consistency*
27	howsoever *in any case*
	admirable *to cause amazement, wonderful*

ACT FIVE

Scene 1. *Enter* THESEUS, HIPPOLYTA, PHILOSTRATE, LORDS, *and* ATTENDANTS

HIPPOLYTA 'Tis strange, my Theseus, that these
    lovers speak of.
THESEUS More strange than true. I never may believe
    These antique fables nor these fairy toys.
    Lovers and madmen have such seething
      brains,
    Such shaping fantasies, that apprehend
    More than cool reason ever comprehends.
    The lunatic, the lover, and the poet
    Are of imagination all compact.
    One sees more devils than vast hell can hold:
    That is the madman. The lover, all as frantic,   10
    Sees Helen's beauty in a brow of Egypt.
    The poet's eye, in a fine frenzy rolling,
    Doth glance from heaven to earth, from earth
      to heaven;
    And as imagination bodies forth
    The forms of things unknown, the poet's
      pen
    Turns them to shapes, and gives to airy
      nothing
    A local habitation and a name.
    Such tricks hath strong imagination
    That if it would but apprehend some joy
    It comprehends some bringer of that joy;   20
    Or in the night, imagining some fear,
    How easy is a bush supposed a bear?
HIPPOLYTA But all the story of the night told over,
    And all their minds transfigured so together,
    More witnesseth than fancy's images,
    And grows to something of great constancy;
    But howsoever, strange and admirable.

Enter the Lovers: LYSANDER, DEMETRIUS, HERMIA,
and HELENA

THESEUS Here come the lovers, full of joy and mirth.
   Joy, gentle friends, joy and fresh days of love
   Accompany your hearts.
LYSANDER   More than to us   30
   Wait in your royal walks, your board, your bed.
THESEUS Come now, what masques, what dances shall
    we have
   To wear away this long age of three hours
   Between our after-supper and bedtime?
   Where is our usual manager of mirth?
   What revels are in hand? Is there no play
   To ease the anguish of a torturing hour?
   Call Philostrate.
PHILOSTRATE [*Coming forward*] Here, mighty Theseus.
THESEUS Say, what abridgement have you for this
    evening?
   What masque? What music? How shall we
    beguile   40
   The lazy time if not with some delight?
PHILOSTRATE [*Giving a paper*] There is a brief how
    many sports are ripe.
   Make choice of which your Highness will see
    first.
THESEUS *The Battle with the Centaurs,* 'to be sung
   By an Athenian eunuch to the harp.'
   We'll none of that. That have I told my love
   In glory of my kinsman Hercules.
   The riot of the tipsy Bacchanals,
   Tearing the Thracian singer in their rage.
   That is an old device, and it was played   50
   When I from Thebes came last a conqueror.
   The thrice three Muses mourning for the death
   Of Learning, late deceased in beggary.
   That is some satire keen and critical,

149

55   sorting with *appropriate to, suitable for*

59   strange *Some scholars have felt dissatisfied with this adjective as not providing a desirable opposition to 'snow' comparable with 'hot ice', 'discord/concord', 'tedious/brief'. However, there is no strong reason for a change.*

65   fitted *i.e. suitable in his rôle*

70   passion *The word could be used for intense feeling of any kind.*

74   unbreathed *unexercised, untrained*

75   against *in preparation for*

77   not for you *not suitable for you*

79   intents *intentions*

80   Extremely . . . pain *exerted by real agony of effort and learned by heart with enormous difficulty*

82   amiss *wrong*

83   simpleness *ingenuousness, innocent sincerity*
            tender *offer, present*

Not sorting with a nuptial ceremony.
A tedious brief scene of young Pyramus
And his love Thisbe; 'very tragical mirth.'
Merry and tragical? Tedious and brief?
That is hot ice and wondrous strange snow.
How shall we find the concord of this discord? 60

PHILOSTRATE A play there is, my lord, some ten words
  long,
Which is as 'brief' as I have known a play –
But by ten words, my lord, it is too long,
Which makes it 'tedious'. For in all the play
There is not one word apt, one player fitted.
And 'tragical', my noble lord, it is,
For Pyramus therein doth kill himself.
Which when I saw rehearsed, I must confess,
Made mine eyes water; but more 'merry' tears
The passion of loud laughter never shed. 70

THESEUS What are they that do play it?

PHILOSTRATE Hard-handed men that work in Athens
  here,
Which never laboured in their minds till now;
And now have toiled their unbreathed
  memories
With this same play against your nuptial.

THESEUS And we will hear it.

PHILOSTRATE   No, my noble lord,
It is not for you. I have heard it over,
And it is nothing, nothing in the world,
Unless you can find sport in their intents,
Extremely stretched and conned with cruel
  pain,   80
To do you service.

THESEUS   I will hear that play,
For never anything can be amiss
When simpleness and duty tender it.
Go bring them in; and take your places, ladies.
                              [*Exit* PHILOSTRATE

85   wretchedness o'ercharged *creatures poor in social position and intellect overburdened by an undertaking which is beyond them*

86   duty . . . perishing *dutiful effort failing in its attempts to please*

88   in this kind *in this sort of thing*

90   take *take in good part*

91   respect *consideration*

92   Takes . . . merit *Take into consideration the effort made not the quality of the finished product*

93   Where I have come *The places I have visited*
       clerks *scholars*

96   periods *pauses*

97   Throttle . . . accent *Permit their nervousness to stifle their highly trained rhetorical delivery*

101   modesty of fearful duty *the modesty displayed by the orators whose devotion to duty made them nervous*

104   simplicity *artlessness*

105   In least *In uttering least*
       to my capacity *in my opinion, according to my understanding of the matter*

106   is addressed *is ready*

107   Flourish of trumpets *This appears in only one of the early texts of the play, but probably indicates the practice of Shakespeare's Company.*

108–17   If we offend . . . know *The device of creating comedy by mispunctuation was an old stage trick by Shakespeare's time. The most famous example in earlier drama occurs in* Ralph Roister Doister (c. 1553), *a play written for performance by schoolboys.*

HIPPOLYTA I love not to see wretchedness o'ercharged,
    And duty in his service perishing.

THESEUS   Why, gentle sweet, you shall see no such
    thing.

HIPPOLYTA He says they can do nothing in this kind.

THESEUS   The kinder we, to give them thanks for
    nothing.

    Our sport shall be to take what they mistake; 90
    And what poor duty cannot do, noble respect
    Takes it in might, not merit.
    Where I have come, great clerks have purposèd
    To greet me with premeditated welcomes,
    Where I have seen them shiver and look pale,
    Make periods in the midst of sentences,
    Throttle their practised accent in their fears,
    And, in conclusion, dumbly have broke off,
    Not paying me a welcome. Trust me, sweet,
    Out of this silence yet I picked a welcome, 100
    And in the modesty of fearful duty
    I read as much as from the rattling tongue
    Of saucy and audacious eloquence.
    Love, therefore, and tongue-tied simplicity
    In least speak most, to my capacity.

Enter PHILOSTRATE

PHILOSTRATE So please your Grace the Prologue is
    addressed.

THESEUS   Let him approach.

    Flourish of trumpets. Enter QUINCE *as Prologue*

QUINCE as Prologue *If we offend, it is with our good will.*
    That you should think we come not to offend
    But with good will. To show our simple skill, 110
    That is the true beginning of our end.
    Consider then we come but in despite.
    We do not come as minding to content you,
    Our true intent is. All for your delight
    We are not here. That you should here repent you

116   show *This may suggest that the mechanicals here perform a dumb-show version of the action of the
Pyramus and Thisbe story. This was a common
practice in plays of the 1560's and 1570's which
Shakespeare is making fun of here.*

118   doth not stand upon points *takes no notice of punctuation marks. There is a pun on 'points' meaning
'small matters, trifles'.*

119   rid *ridden; with a pun on 'rid' meaning divested'.*

120   the stop *the full stop; with a pun on 'stop' meaning
'the sudden reining in of a horse'.*

123   government *control, proper management*

127   Gentles *This was the normal address for 'Ladies and
gentlemen'.*
    wonder *are amazed*

130   certain *Shakespeare places the accent archaically on
the second syllable.*

136   Presenteth *represents, personates*

139   hight *is named. This was an archaic form in Shakespeare's day.*

142   fall *drop*

144   tall *brave, courageous*

145   his trusty ... slain *The grammar is deliberately
obscure for comic effect.*

154

The actors are at hand; and by their show
You shall know all that you are like to know.

THESEUS   This fellow doth not stand upon points.

LYSANDER   He hath rid his prologue like a rough colt;
he knows not the stop. A good moral, my lord: it is   120
not enough to speak, but to speak true.

HIPPOLYTA Indeed he hath played on his prologue like
a child on a recorder – a sound, but not in government.

THESEUS His speech was like a tangled chain; nothing
impaired, but all disordered. Who is next?

Enter BOTTOM *as* Pyramus, FLUTE *as* Thisbe,
SNOUT *as* Wall, STARVELING *as* Moonshine, *and*
SNUG *as* Lion; *a trumpeter before them*

QUINCE *as* Prologue *Gentles, perchance you wonder at*
this show;
But wonder on, till truth make all things plain.
This man is Pyramus, if you would know;
This beauteous lady Thisbe is certain.   130
This man with lime and roughcast doth present
Wall – that vile wall which did these lovers
sunder;
And through Wall's chink, poor souls, they are
content
To whisper. At the which let no man wonder.
This man with lantern, dog and bush of thorn
Presenteth Moonshine. For, if you will know,
By moonshine did these lovers think no scorn
To meet at Ninus' tomb, there, there to woo.
This grisly beast – which Lion hight by name –
The trusty Thisbe coming first by night   140
Did scare away, or rather did affright.
And as she fled, her mantle she did fall,
Which Lion vile with bloody mouth did stain.
Anon comes Pyramus, sweet youth and tall,
And finds his trusty Thisbe's mantle slain.

146–7   with blade ... breast *With this excessively alliteration Shakespeare is parodying the plays of the 1560s and 1570s in which it was a favourite and often over-used poetic device.*

147   bravely *nobly*

          broached *pierced. The association of this word is 'broaching a barrel' and is thus comically inappropriate in this context.*

151   At large *At full length*

152   be to *is going to*

153   asses *This word is obviously carefully chosen.*

154   interlude *entertainment, play*

155   present *represent*

157   crannied *The adjective is, of course, superfluous.*

160   roughcast *a mixture of lime and gravel used to plaster over the outside walls of a house*

          show *demonstrate, symbolise*

162   right and sinister *running right and left, horizontal. The accent in 'sinister' is on the second syllable.*

163   fearful *timid, timorous*

          whisper *The rhyme is imperfect. In modern productions actors often make an effort to correct the rhyme for comic effect by pronouncing the word 'whisisper'.*

164   lime and hair *used in the making of bricks*

166   wittiest *most intelligent*

          partition *The pun is on the two meanings: (1) wall, divider; (2) section of an oration or composition.*

Whereat, with blade – with bloody blameful
   blade –
He bravely broached his boiling bloody breast.
And Thisbe, tarrying in mulberry shade,
His dagger drew, and died. For all the rest,
Let Lion, Moonshine, Wall, and lovers twain   150
At large discourse while here they do remain.

[*Exit* QUINCE, BOTTOM, FLUTE, SNUG, *and* STARVELING

THESEUS   I wonder if the lion be to speak.

DEMETRIUS No wonder, my lord, – one lion may, when
         many asses do.

SNOUT as Wall *In this same interlude it doth befall*
      That I – one Snout by name – present a wall.
      And such a wall, as I would have you think,
      That had in it a crannied hole or chink,
      Through which the lovers, Pyramus and Thisbe,
      Did whisper often, very secretly.
      This loam, this roughcast, and this stone doth
         show   160
      That I am that same wall: the truth is so.
      And this the cranny is, right and sinister,
      Through which the fearful lovers are to whisper.

THESEUS   Would you desire lime and hair to speak
         better?

DEMETRIUS It is the wittiest partition that ever I heard
   discourse, my lord.

               Enter BOTTOM *as Pyramus*

THESEUS Pyramus draws near the wall. Silence!

BOTTOM as Pyramus *O grim-looked night, O night with*
      hue so black,
   O night, which ever art when day is not!
   O night, O night, alack, alack, alack,   170
   I fear my Thisbe's promise is forgot.
   And thou, O wall, O sweet, O lovely wall,
   That stand'st between her father's ground and
      mine,

180   sensible *conscious, capable of feeling*
       should *ought to*
181   again *in reply, in return*
182 ff. No, in truth . . . *It is noticeable that although all the*
       actors have been baited by the audience only Bottom
       sets them right.
182   should not *was not to*
185   fall *happen*
       pat *exactly, precisely*

191   an *if*

194   lover's grace *gracious lover*
195   Limander *Bottom confuses two Classical lovers:*
       Leander the beloved of Hero, and Alexander (or
       Paris) the lover of Helen of Troy.
       still *always, ever*
197   Not Shafalus . . . true *Bottom means Cephalus and*
       Procris, whose story is told in Book VII of Ovid's
       Metamorphoses.
201   Ninny's *Despite Quince's attempt at correction in III.*
       1. 95, Bottom has still not learned the correct pro-
       nunciation of the name.
       straightway *immediately*

158

Thou wall, O wall, O sweet and lovely wall,
Show me thy chink, to blink through with mine
eyne.

SNOUT *holds up his fingers*

Thanks, courteous wall; Jove shield thee well for
this.
But what see I? No Thisbe do I see.
O wicked wall, through whom I see no bliss,
Cursed be thy stones for thus deceiving me!

THESEUS The wall, methinks, being sensible, should 180
curse again.

BOTTOM No, in truth, sir, he should not. 'Deceiving
me' is Thisbe's cue. She is to enter now, and I am
to spy her through the wall. You shall see — it will
fall pat as I told you. Yonder she comes.

Enter FLUTE *as* Thisbe

FLUTE as Thisbe *O wall, full often hast thou heard my*
moans
For parting my fair Pyramus and me.
My cherry lips have often kissed thy stones,
Thy stones with lime and hair knit up in thee.

BOTTOM as Pyramus *I see a voice. Now will I to the chink* 190
To spy an I can hear my Thisbe's face.
Thisbe!

FLUTE as Thisbe *My love! Thou art my love, I think?*

BOTTOM as Pyramus *Think what thou wilt, I am thy*
lover's grace;
And like Limander am I trusty still.

FLUTE as Thisbe *And I like Helen till the Fates me kill.*

BOTTOM as Pyramus *Not Shafalus to Procrus was so true.*

FLUTE as Thisbe *As Shafalus to Procrus, I to you.*

BOTTOM as Pyramus *O, kiss me through the hole of this*
vile wall!

FLUTE as Thisbe *I kiss the wall's hole, not your lips at all.* 200

BOTTOM as Pyramus *Wilt thou at Ninny's tomb meet me*
straightway?

202   Tide . . . death *Come life, come death*

203   dischargèd *performed*

205   mural down *All of the early texts of the play are con-*
           fused at this point. This emendation was made by the
           eighteenth-century poet, Alexander Pope.
206   No remedy *There is no help for it*
           to *as to*
207   hear without warning *to listen into a plot and not warn*
           their owners (i.e. the parents) of it (?)
209   The best in this kind *i.e. even the finest actors*
210   amend them *make good their deficiencies*

216 ff.   You, Ladies . . . *This speech is the result of the discus-*
           sion at III. 1. 25–42. It has also encouraged scholars
           to cite a contemporary event at the Scottish court on
           30 August 1594. At the baptismal celebrations of
           Prince Henry, the son of James VI, a triumphal car
           was drawn into the hall by a blackamoor, instead of
           by the originally intended lion, which it was thought
           would run wild or frighten the audience.
221   fell *The pun is on the two meanings: (1) fierce, angry;*
           (2) skin coat.
           lion's dam *lioness*
223   'twere . . . life *my life would be in danger (from*
           punishment)
224   gentle *polite*
226   best *The pun is with 'beast'.*

227   a very fox . . . valour *i.e. he is more crafty than brave*

FLUTE as Thisbe *Tide life, tide death, I come without delay.*

                        [Exeunt BOTTOM *and* FLUTE

SNOUT as Wall *Thus have I, Wall, my part dischargèd so;*
       And, being done, thus Wall away doth go.

                                    [Exit

THESEUS   Now is the mural down between the two neighbours.

DEMETRIUS No remedy, my lord, when walls are so wilful to hear without warning.

HIPPOLYTA This is the silliest stuff that ever I heard.

THESEUS   The best in this kind are but shadows; and the worst are no worse, if imagination amend them. 210

HIPPOLYTA It must be your imagination then, and not theirs.

THESEUS   If we imagine no worse of them than they of themselves, they may pass for excellent men.
Here come two noble beasts in: a man and a lion.

Enter SNUG as Lion *and* STARVELING as Moonshine

SNUG as Lion *You, ladies – you whose gentle hearts do fear*
       The smallest monstrous mouse that creeps on floor
       May now, perchance, both quake and tremble here,
       When lion rough in wildest rage doth roar.
       Then know that I as Snug the joiner am   220
       A lion fell, nor else no lion's dam;
       For if I should as lion come in strife
       Into this place, 'twere pity on my life.

THESEUS   A very gentle beast, and of a good conscience.

DEMETRIUS The very best at a beast, my lord, that e'er I saw.

LYSANDER   This lion is a very fox for his valour.

THESEUS   True; and a goose for his discretion.

230 carry *conquer*
   carries *carries off*

234 lanthorn *lantern; with a pun on 'horned' as the pronunciation was 'lant-horn'.*
235 present *represent*
236 He should . . . head *Horns were considered to be the
   sign of a cuckold (deceived husband).*
   crescent *a waxing moon*

243 for *for fear of*
244 in snuff *The pun is on the two meanings: (1) in need of
   snuffing; (2) in a bad temper.*

248 stay the time *wait for the time to pass*

250–52 All that . . . dog *Starveling is so exasperated by the
   interruptions that he drops his rôle and speaks in his
   own person.*

255 Ninny's *Flute is obviously more influenced by Bottom's
   erroneous pronunciation of the name than by Quince's
   earlier correction. See the note to l. 201 above.*

DEMETRIUS Not so, my lord; for his valour cannot
    carry his discretion; and the fox carries the goose.   230

THESEUS   His discretion, I am sure, cannot carry his
    valour; for the goose carries not the fox. It is well:
    leave it to his discretion, and let us listen to the
    moon.

STARVELING as Moonshine *This lanthorn doth the hornèd*
        moon present —

DEMETRIUS He should have worn the horns on his head.

THESEUS   He is no crescent, and his horns are in-
    visible within the circumference.

STARVELING as Moonshine *This lanthorn doth the hornèd*
        moon present.
        Myself the man i' th' moon do seem to be.

THESEUS   This is the greatest error of all the rest; the   240
    man should be put into the lanthorn. How is it else
    the man i' th' moon?

DEMETRIUS He dares not come there, for the candle;
    for, you see, it is already in snuff.

HIPPOLYTA I am aweary of this moon. Would he would
    change!

THESEUS   It appears by his small light of discretion
    that he is in the wane. But yet, in courtesy, in all
    reason, we must stay the time.

LYSANDER Proceed, Moon,

STARVELING All that I have to say is to tell you that the   250
    lanthorn is the moon, I the man i' th' moon, this
    thornbrush my thornbrush, and this dog my dog.

DEMETRIUS Why, all these should be in the lanthorn;
    for all these are in the moon. But silence: here comes
    Thisbe.

Enter FLUTE *as* Thisbe

FLUTE as Thisbe *This is old Ninny's tomb. Where is my*
        love?

SNUG as Lion *O!*   [*He roars and* FLUTE *runs off*

DEMETRIUS Well roared, Lion!

262   moused *The reference is to Snug's shaking of Thisbe's mantle, which obviously resembles a cat shaking a dead mouse.*

265   beams *Some scholars have suggested that the early texts of the play are wrong here, and that the reading should be 'gleams' for the sake of alliteration.*

269   spite *disaster, vexation*

271   dole *reason for sorrow*

277   Furies *These were creatures in Greek mythology who pursued mortals, usually the guilty. In the tragic drama of the 1560s and 1570s modelled on the Latin plays of Seneca invocations to the Furies were quite common.*
               fell *fierce*

278–9   O Fates . . . thrum *In Greek mythology the three Fates or Parchae were Lachesis, who spun the thread of man's life, Clotho, who carried the distaff and measured the thread, and Atropos, who cut the thread when the weaving was complete.*

279   thread and thrum *everything. The 'thread' is the warp in weaving, and the 'thrum' is the tufted end of the warp. The information is specialised knowledge related to Bottom's trade.*

280   Quail *Destroy, overcome*
               quell *kill*

281   passion *'emotional suffering' and 'passionate speech'*

283   Beshrew *Curse (in a light-hearted way)*

285   deflowered *ravished, carried off*

287   cheer *face, countenance*

288   confound *destroy me*

164

THESEUS   Well run, Thisbe!

HIPPOLYTA Well shone, Moon! Truly, the moon shines   260
with a good grace.

          [SNUG as Lion *tears* Thisbe's *mantle and exits*

THESEUS   Well moused, Lion!

DEMETRIUS And then came Pyramus.

LYSANDER   And so the lion vanished.

Enter BOTTOM *as* Pyramus

BOTTOM as Pyramus *Sweet moon, I thank thee for thy*
    sunny beams;
      I thank thee, moon, for shining now so bright;
      For, by thy gracious, golden, glittering beams
      I trust to take of truest Thisbe sight.
          But stay – O spite!
          But mark, poor knight,   270
      What dreadful dole is here!
          Eyes, do you see? –
          How can it be?
      O dainty duck, O dear!
          Thy mantle good –
      What, stained with blood?
      Approach, ye Furies fell!
          O Fates, come, come,
          Cut thread and thrum,
      Quail, crush, conclude, and quell!   280

THESEUS This passion, and the death of a dear friend,
would go near to make a man look sad.

HIPPOLYTA Beshrew my heart but I pity the man.

BOTTOM as Pyramus   *O, wherefore, Nature, didst*
    thou lions frame?
      Since lion vile hath here deflowered my dear?
    Which is – no, no! which was – the fairest dame
      That lived, that loved, that liked, that looked
      with cheer.
          Come, tears, confound;
          Out, sword, and wound

290   pap *breast*

299   die *one of a pair of dice*
         ace *the spot on a dice*

304   ass *The pun is with 'ace' in l. 299.*
305   How chance *How comes it about that*

308   passion *highly charged emotional speech*

311   mote *speck. See note to III. 1. 161.*

313   God warr'nt *God defend*

316   means *Probably two meanings intended here: (1) lays
         a formal complaint; (2) laments.*
         videlicet *a legal term meaning 'thus it may be seen'*

321   tomb *The pronunciation of the time makes this a
         correct rhyme with 'dumb'.*

166

>   The pap of Pyramus: 290
>   Ay, that left pap
>   Where heart doth hop.
>   Thus die I, thus, thus, thus.

>   [*He stabs himself*

>   Now am I dead,
>   Now am I fled;
>   My soul is in the sky.
>   Tongue, lose thy light,
>   Moon, take they flight;

>   [*Exit* STARVELING

>   Now die, die, die, die, die.   [*He dies*

DEMETRIUS No die, but an ace, for him! For he is but
one.   300

LYSANDER Less than an ace, man; for he is dead, he is
nothing.

THESEUS With the help of a surgeon he might yet
recover, and yet prove an ass.

HIPPOLYTA How chance Moonshine is gone before
Thisbe comes back and finds her lover?

THESEUS She will find him by starlight. Here she
comes; and her passion ends the play.

Enter FLUTE *as* Thisbe

HIPPOLYTA Methinks she should not use a long one for
such a Pyramus. I hope she will be brief.   310

DEMETRIUS A mote will turn the balance which
Pyramus, which Thisbe is the better – he for a man,
God warr'nt us! – she for a woman, God bless us!

LYSANDER She hath spied him already with those
sweet eyes.

DEMETRIUS And thus she means, videlicet:

FLUTE as Thisbe   *Asleep, my love?*
>   What, dead, my dove?
>   O Pyramus, arise!
>   Speak, speak! Quite dumb?   320
>   Dead, dead? A tomb

329   Sisters three *the Fates: Clotho, Lachesis, and Atropos.*
        See note to ll. 278–9. This passage resembles some
        lines in Cambises *a play written by Thomas Preston*
        in 1569 and is one of the type which Shakespeare
        seems to be parodying in the playlet.

333   shore *shorn; the form is for the sake of the rhyme.*

336   Come trusty sword *A passage in a play* The Fleire
        written by Edward Sharpham in 1607 appears to
        refer to a piece of contemporary stage business at this
        point, in which Flute as Thisbe almost impales him-
        self with the scabbard rather than the sword.

337   imbrue *stain with blood*

341   left *left behind*

345   Bergomask *a grotesque dance similar to that popular*
        among the peasants of Berganio, Italy.

350   Marry *A mild oath meaning originally 'By the Virgin*
        Mary'.

353   And so ... discharged *Theseus here charitably appre-*
        ciates the mechanicals' performance, presumably in
        response to their disappointment registered at previ-
        ous remarks.
    discharged *performed*

> Must cover thy sweet eyes.
> These lily lips,
> This cherry nose,
> These yellow cowslip cheeks,
> Are gone, are gone.
> Lovers, make moan –
> His eyes were green as leeks.
> O Sisters three,
> Come, come to me   330
> With hands as pale as milk;
> Lay them in gore,
> Since you have shore
> With shears his thread of silk.
> Tongue, not a word!
> Come, trusty sword,
> Come, blade, my breast imbrue!
> >   [*She stabs herself*
> And farewell, friends.
> Thus Thisbe ends.
> Adieu, adieu, adieu.   [*She dies*   340

Enter SNUG *as* Lion, STARVELING *as* Moonshine, *and* SNOUT *as* Wall

THESEUS   Moonshine and Lion are left to bury the dead.

DEMETRIUS   Ay, and Wall too.

BOTTOM [*Jumping up*] No, I assure you; the wall is down that parted their fathers. Will it please you to see the epilogue, or to hear a Bergomask dance between two of our company?

THESEUS   No epilogue, I pray you; for your play needs no excuse. Never excuse; for when the players are all dead, there need none to be blamed. Marry, if he 350 that writ it had played Pyramus and hanged himself in Thisbe's garter, it would have been a fine tragedy. And so it is truly, and very notably discharged. But, come, your Bergomask. Let your epilogue alone.

Exeunt ... Snout *This does not appear in any of the early texts of the play, but it is obviously necessary in view of Theseus's remarks at l. 354.*

355 told *counted, struck*

356 fairy time *i.e. from midnight to dawn*

358 overwatched *stayed up late. See the note on the title.*

359 palpable-gross *the crudeness of which is obvious*

359–60 beguiled ... night *diverted our attention pleasurably from the slow-moving passage of time during the evening*

361 solemnity *festive celebration*

362 revels *amusements, entertainments*

Enter Puck *In modern productions this is often effected by the use of a trapdoor.*

364 behowls *The early texts of the play all have 'beholds' here, but the notion of wolves howling at the moon was sufficiently common to justify the change.*

365 heavy *i.e. with weariness*

366 fordone *worn out, exhausted*

367 wasted *used-up, burnt-out*

brands *logs of wood used for firewood*

368 screech owl *This was considered a bird of ill-omen.*

373 Every one *i.e. of the graves*

sprite *ghost, spirit*

376 triple Hecate's team *The goddess Hecate had three identities: Luna or Cynthia in heaven, Diana on earth, and Proserpina or Hecate in Hell.*

379 frolic *frolicsome, merry*

382 To sweep ... door *This was one of the tasks associated with Robin Goodfellow.*

behind *meaning 'from behind' where the dust had been swept by careless maidservants.*

A dance

[*Exeunt* BOTTOM, FLUTE, SNUG, STARVELING, *and* SNOUT

The iron tongue of midnight hath told twelve.
Lovers, to bed; 'tis almost fairy time.
I fear we shall outsleep the coming morn
As much as we this night have overwatched.
This palpable-gross play hath well beguiled
The heavy gait of night. Sweet friends, to bed. 360
A fortnight hold we this solemnity
In nightly revels and new jollity.

[*Exeunt*

Enter PUCK *with a broom*

PUCK   Now the hungry lion roars,
      And the wolf behowls the moon,
Whilst the heavy ploughman snores,
      All with weary task fordone.
Now the wasted brands do glow,
      Whilst the screech owl, screeching loud,
Puts the wretch that lies in woe
      In remembrance of a shroud. 370
Now it is the time of night
      That the graves, all gaping wide,
Every one lets forth his sprite,
      In the churchway paths to glide.
And we fairies, that do run
      By the triple Hecate's team,
From the presence of the sun,
      Following darkness like a dream,
Now are frolic. Not a mouse
Shall disturb this hallowed house. 380
I am sent with broom before
To sweep the dust behind the door.

Enter OBERON *and* TITANIA, *with all their Train*

OBERON Through the house give glimmering light
      By the dead and drowsy fire;

386   ditty *song*

388   rehearse . . . rote *go over your song from memory*

         song *There are two possibilities here: (1) either there is a separate song sung during the dance; (2) or Oberon's lines 392 ff. is the song.*

394   best bride-bed *i.e. that of Theseus and Hippolyta*

396   create *conceived, created*

401   issue *children*
403   mark prodigious *a birthmark indicating bad luck in life*

406   consecrate *blessed, consecrated*
407   take his gait *make his way*
408   several *separate*

414   shadows *The double allusion is to the fairies and to the actors.*

              Every elf and fairy sprite
              Hop as light as bird from brier;
              And this ditty, after me,
              Sing, and dance it trippingly.

TITANIA   First rehearse your song by rote,
              To each word a warbling note.
              Hand in hand with fairy grace   390
              Will we sing and bless this place.

                  Song and dance

OBERON   Now, until the break of day,
              Through this house each fairy stray.
              To the best bride-bed will we,
              Which by us shall blessèd be;
              And the issue there create
              Ever shall be fortunate.
              So shall all the couples three
              Ever true in loving be,
              And the blots of Nature's hand   400
              Shall not in their issue stand.
              Never mole, harelip, nor scar,
              Nor mark prodigious, such as are
              Despisèd in nativity,
              Shall upon their children be.
              With this field-dew consecrate,
              Every fairy take his gait,
              And each several chamber bless,
              Through this palace, with sweet peace;
              And the owner of it blessed   410
              Ever shall in safety rest.
              Trip away; make no stay;
              Meet me all by break of day.

             [*Exeunt* OBERON, TITANIA, *and their Train*

PUCK [*To the audience*]
              If we shadows have offended,
              Think but this, and all is mended –
              That you have but slumbered here
              While these visions did appear.

418   idle *foolish, trifling*
419   no more yielding *offering no more than*
420   Gentles *Ladies and gentlemen*
421   mend *improve*

424   scape *avoid, escape*
         serpent's tongue *hisses (of disapproval from the audience)*

428   Give . . . hands *i.e. Applaud me*
429   restore amends *make improvement*

And this weak and idle theme,
No more yielding but a dream,
Gentles, do not reprehend.   420
If you pardon, we will mend.
And, as I am an honest Puck,
If we have unearnèd luck
Now to scape the serpent's tongue
We will make amends ere long;
Else the Puck a liar call.
So, good night unto you all.
Give me your hands, if we be friends,
And Robin shall restore amends.

                                        [*Exit*

APPENDIX: ELIZABETHAN FAIRIES AND FOLK CUSTOMS

A Midsummer Night's Dream is associated with two traditional occasions of festivity: May Day and Midsummer Eve. The first of these paid homage to the arrival of spring and symbolically reaffirmed a relationship between human and natural cycles. As such it was essentially a fertility rite and thus invariably associated with courtship and marriage. A Puritan writer of Shakespeare's time, John Stubbes, gives perhaps the most vivid picture of the form its celebration took in sixteenth-century England:

> Against May ... all the young men and maids, old men and wives, run gadding overnight to the woods, groves, hills, and mountains, where they spend all night in pleasant pastimes; and in the morning they return, bringing with them birch and branches of trees to deck their assemblies withall. ... But the chiefest jewel they bring from thence is their Maypole, which they bring home with great veneration, as thus: they have twenty or forty yoke of oxen, every ox having a sweet nose-gay of flowers placed on the tip of his horns. And these oxen draw home this May-pole which is all covered with flowers and herbs, bound round about with strings from the top to the bottom, and sometimes painted with variable colours, with two or three hundred men, women, and children following it with great devotion. And being thus reared up with handkerchiefs and flags hovering on the top, they straw the ground round about, bind green boughs about it, set up summer halls, bowers, and arbors hard by it. And then they fall to dance about it, like as the heathen people did at the dedication of the idols.

The holiday of the play's title is one of the oldest and most popular of the pagan rites observed in sixteenth-century England. It was originally a worshipping of the sun at the peak of his summer powers; but by Shakespeare's time it had become a night of rural festivity associated with magic and enchantment. The rituals connected with it were numerous and included all-night vigils in woods and fields; the collecting of herbs and flowers which were believed to be able to cure sickness or bring luck or reveal one's future lover; the building of fires; and the carrying of torches in procession. It was a time also when illusions were common, and when mischievous spirits were abroad playing strange tricks upon humans. One of the most notorious of these was the misleading of men and animals by the sprite's becoming a 'fool's fire' or will-o-the-wisp or assuming a trick voice to lure unwary travellers into swamps and ponds.

It is through his special association with his kind of mischief that the Puck or Robin Goodfellow is naturally a part of the Midsummer Night's happenings. A ballad of the time describes this aspect of his activities in language very similar to that used by Shakespeare in his play:

> Sometimes he'd counterfeit a voice,
> And travellers call astray.
> Sometimes a walking fire he'd be
> And lead them from their way.

Robin Goodfellow's pranks were not, however, restricted to any special season. He was a lone creature, variously called puck, bugbear, pixie, hobgoblin, who was not traditionally connected with the fairy world and certainly owed no allegiance to its king Oberon. He was the best-known elf of sixteenth-century rural England, whose activities are best described in the speeches of the First Fairy and himself soon after his entrance in II. 1: the frightening of young girls, the skimming of milk, the misleading of travellers, the causing of harmless accidents, and the helping or frustrating of servants and farmers. While he was considered in general as a harmless – if mischievous – country elf, the English attitude to him had in it also the element of fear which associated him with ghosts, witches, and other less friendly supernatural beings, and which is reflected in the play in his speech to Oberon at III. 2. 385–94.

Prior to the composition of *A Midsummer Night's Dream* the fairies of literary tradition were either human or superhuman in stature; but their country counterparts were of various dimensions ranging from the giant Cornish spriggans to elves no bigger than an insect and including female spirits who married mortal men. To most of rural England the commonest version was of a smaller than man-sized being, perhaps three feet tall, who could provoke words like 'little', 'puppet', and 'manikin' which are used of Oberon in a play written some three or four years earlier than Shakespeare's. But there is some evidence that in Warwickshire as elsewhere in England, miniscule creatures who can sleep in flower-heads were commonly thought of.

The Elizabethan literary treatment of fairies suggests no great fear of them on the part of Englishmen of the time, although like Puck they were often lumped together with supernatural creatures of vicious propensities and like these had their natural habitat in the night. But usually they were thought of as dancing creatures whose worst crimes were the pinching, pricking, and misleading of mortals. The action most commonly attributed to them was the stealing of human babies and the substituting of changelings, which according to contemporary evidence was a real fear among country people.

In the light of these beliefs one can see that, though firmly rooted in English country superstitions, Shakespeare's supernatural world in *A Midsummer Night's Dream* is a construct of mixed elements drived from both literary and oral traditions of wood spirits, household elves, local goblins, infernal beings, and classical deities.

Its uniqueness lies in the way these various elements have been welded together and given a vivid and concrete existence by the dramatist's poetic imagination so that it has become the *only* fairy world of the English-speaking nations.